BDC

Handbook of

GENERAL
ANATOMY

MW00843951

Titika Sachdeva

Late Dr B D Chaurasia
1937–1985

B D Chaurasia'S
Handbook of
GENERAL
ANATOMY

Fourth Edition

Late Dr B D Chaurasia
MBBS, MS, PhD, FAMS

Department of Anatomy
G.R. Medical College
Gwalior, India

CBS PUBLISHERS & DISTRIBUTORS PVT. LTD.
New Delhi • Bangalore • Pune • Cochin • Chennai (India)

ISBN: 978-81-239-1654-5

First Edition: 1978
Reprint: 1980, 1981
Second Edition: 1983
Reprint: 1985, 1987, 1989, 1991, 1992, 1994, 1996
Third Edition: 1996
Reprint: 1998, 1999, 2000, 2001, 2002, 2003, 2004
Fourth Edition: 2009
Reprint: 2010

Copyright © 1978, 1983, 1996, 2008, Publishers and Author

Third and Fourth Editions revised by
Dr. Krishna Garg
Ex-Professor and Head, Department of Anatomy,
Lady Hardinge Medical College, New Delhi-110 001, India

All rights reserved. No part of this book may be reproduced or transmitted in any form or by any means, electronic or mechanical, including photocopying, recording, or any information storage and retrieval system, without permission, in writing, from the author and the publisher.

Published by Satish Kumar Jain and produced by Vinod Kumar Jain for
CBS Publishers & Distributors Pvt. Ltd.,
4819/XI, 24 Ansari Road, Daryaganj, New Delhi 110 002, India.
Ph: 23289259, 23266861/67 • Fax: +91-011-23243014
e-mail: delhi@cbspd.com, cbspubs@vsnl.com
Website: www.cbspd.com

Branches:

* *Bengaluru:* Seema House 2975, 17th Cross, K.R. Road, Banasankari
  2nd Stage, Bengaluru-560 070, Karnataka • Ph: +91-80-26771678/79
  Fax: +91-80-26771680 • e-mail: bangalore@cbspd.com
* *Pune:* Bhuruk Prestige, Sr. No. 52/12/2+1+3/2 Narhe, Haveli
  (Near Katraj-Dehu Road Bypass), Pune-411 051, Maharashtra
  Ph: 020-64704058–59, 020-32342277 • Fax: 020-24300160
  e-mail: pune@cbspd.com
* *Kochi:* 36/14 Kalluvilakam, Lissie Hospital Road, Kochi-682 018, Kerala
  Ph: +91-484-4059061-65 • Fax: +91-484-4059065
* *Chennai:* 20, West Park Road, Shenoy Nagar, Chennai-600 030, Tamil Nadu
  Ph: 91-44-26260666, 26208620 • Fax: 91-44 45530020 • chennai@cbspd.com

Printed at: SDR Printers Pvt. Ltd., Delhi 110094 (India)

Preface to the Fourth Edition

I feel a sense of pride and enthusiasm in presenting to you the fourth edition of this popular book. Now, simple coloured diagrams extensively illustrate each chapter. Once initial interest to read text supplemented by diagrams is developed, learning general anatomy is hardly problematic.

Clinical anatomy has been illustrated with coloured diagrams. Students have always been encouraging me in improving both text and diagrams.

The help of Ms. Priya, MBBS student of Lady Hardinge Medical College during 1990–91, is being acknowledged for improving the "Anatomical word meanings and historical names."

Mr. Ajit Kumar, first year student of Banarasidas Chandiwala Institute of Physiotherapy (BCIP) 2004–05, gave constructive suggestions for its betterment. Ms. Stuti Malhotra, first year student of BCIP (2007–08), provided me with a number of tables in various chapters. I feel highly obliged to them.

The editor is obliged to Mr. Y.N. Arjuna, Publishing Director, CBS for timely and much needed guidance. Page layout and four colour diagrams work have been diligently done by Ms. Nishi Verma and Mr. Chand Singh Naagar of M/s. Limited Colors.

Mr. Vinod Jain, Production Director, and Mr. Satish Jain, Chairman, CBS Publishers and Distributors, have been helping me from time to time. Comments from the students are welcome.

Krishna Garg
Editor

dedicated
to
my teacher
Shri Uma Shankar Nagayach

Preface to the First Edition

This handbook of general anatomy has been written to meet the requirements of students who are newly admitted to medical colleges. It thoroughly introduces the greater part of medical terminology, as well as the various structures which constitute the human body. On account of the late admissions and the shorter time now available for teaching anatomy, the coverage of general anatomy seems to suffer maximum. Since it lays down the foundation of the entire subject of medicine, it was felt necessary to produce a short, simple and comprehensive handbook on this neglected, though important, aspect of the subject. It has been written in a simple language, with the text classified in small parts to make it easier for the students to follow and remember. It is hoped that this will prove quite useful to the medical students.

Gwalior
November 1978

B D CHAURASIA

Contents

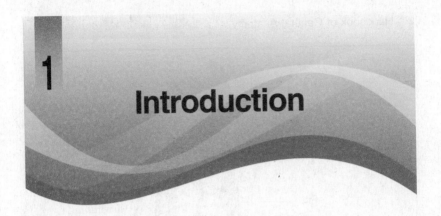

Introduction

Human anatomy is the science which deals with the structure of the human body. The term, 'anatomy', is derived from a Greek word, "anatome", meaning cutting up. The term 'dissection' is a Latin equivalent of the Greek anatome. However, the two words, anatomy and dissection, are not synonymous. Dissection is a mere technique, whereas anatomy is a wide field of study.

Anatomy forms firm foundation of the whole art of medicine and introduces the student to the greater part of medical terminology. "Anatomy is to physiology as geography is to history, i.e. it describes the theatre in which the action takes place."

SUBDIVISIONS OF ANATOMY

Initially, anatomy was studied mainly by dissection. But the scope of modern anatomy has become very wide because it is now studied by all possible techniques which can enlarge the boundaries of the anatomical knowledge.

The main subdivisions of anatomy are:

1. **Cadaveric anatomy** is studied on dead embalmed (preserved) bodies usually with the naked eye (macroscopic or gross anatomy). This can be done by one of the two approaches: (a) In '*regional anatomy*' the body is studied in parts, like the upper limb, lower limb, thorax, abdomen, head and neck, and brain; (b) in '*systemic anatomy*' the body is studied in systems, like the skeletal system (osteology) (Fig. 1.1), muscular system (myology), articulatory system (arthrology or syndesmology), vascular system (angiology), nervous system (neurology), and respiratory, digestive, urogenital and endocrine systems (splanchnology). The locomotor system includes osteology, arthrology and myology.

Fig. 1.1: Skeletal system

2. **Living Anatomy** is studied by inspection, palpation (Fig. 1.2), percussion, auscultation, endoscopy (bronchoscopy, gastroscopy), radiography, electromyography, etc.

Fig. 1.2: Contracted muscles for palpation

3. **Embryology (developmental anatomy)** is the study of the prenatal developmental changes in an individual. The developmental history is called 'ontogeny'. The evolutionary history on the other hand, is called 'phylogeny'.
4. **Histology (microscopic anatomy)** is the study of structures with the aid of a microscope.
5. **Surface anatomy (topographic anatomy)** is the study of deeper parts of the body in relation to the skin surface. It is helpful in clinical practice and surgical operations (Fig. 1.3).

Fig. 1.3: Palpating the dorsalis pedis artery

6. **Radiographic and imaging anatomy** is the study of the bones and deeper organs by plain and contrast radiography by ultrasound and computerised tomographic (CT) scans (Fig. 1.4).

Fig. 1.4: X-ray of chest (plain radiograph)

7. **Comparative anatomy** is the study of anatomy of the other animals to explain the changes in form, structure and function (morphology) of different parts of the human body.

8. **Physical anthropology** deals with the external features and measurements of different races and groups of people, and with the study of the prehistoric remains.

Fig. 1.5: Physical anthropology

9. **Applied anatomy (clinical anatomy)** deals with application of the anatomical knowledge to the medical and surgical practice (Fig. 1.6).

10. **Experimental anatomy** is the study of the factors which influence and determine the form, structure and function of different parts of the body.

11. **Genetics** deals with the study of information present in the chromosomes.

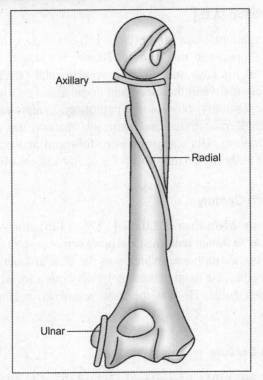

Fig. 1.6: The relation of nerves to the humerus and likelihood of their injury in case of fracture

HISTORY OF ANATOMY

1. Greek Period (B.C.)

Hippocrates of Cos (circa 400 B.C.), the 'Father of Medicine', is regarded as one of the founders of anatomy. Parts of Hippocratic collection are the earliest anatomical descriptions.

Herophilus of Chalcedon (circa 300 B.C.) is called the "father of anatomy". He was a Greek physician, and was one of the first to dissect the human body. He distinguished cerebrum from cerebellum, nerves from tendons, arteries from veins, and the motor from sensory nerves. He described and named the parts of eye, meninges, torcular Herophili, fourth ventricle with calamus scriptorius, hyoid bone, duodenum, prostate gland, etc. We owe to him the first description of the lacteals. Herophilus was a very successful teacher, and wrote a book on anatomy, *A special treatise of the eyes,* and a popular handbook for midwives.

2. Roman Period (A.D.)

Galen of Pergamum, Asia Minor (circa 130–200 A.D.), the "prince of physicians", practised medicine at Rome. He was the foremost' practitioner of his days and the first experimental physiologist. He wrote voluminously and theorized and dogmatized on many medical subjects like anatomy, physiology, pathology, symptomatology and treatment. He demonstrated and wrote on anatomy *De anatomicis-administrationibus*. His teachings were followed and considered as the infallible authority on the subject for nearly 15 centuries.

3. Fourteenth Century

Mundinus or Mondino d'Luzzi (1276–1326), the 'restorer of anatomy', was an Italian anatomist and professor of anatomy at Bologna. He wrote a book *Anathomia* which was the standard anatomical text for over a century. He taught anatomy by dissection for which his text was used as a guide. He was the most renowned anatomist before Vesalius.

4. Fifteenth Century

Leonardo da Vinci of Italy (1452–1519), the originator of cross-sectional anatomy, was one of the greatest geniuses the world has known. He was a master of arts and contributed substantially in mathematics, science and engineering. He was the first to describe the moderator band of the right ventricle. The most admirable of his works are the drawings of the things he observed with perfection and fidelity. His 60 notebooks containing 500 diagrams were published in 1898.

5. Sixteenth Century

Vesalius (1514–1564), the 'reformer of anatomy', was German in origin, Belgian (Brussels) by birth, and found an Italian (Padua) university favourable for his work. He was professor of anatomy at Padua. He is regarded as the founder of modern anatomy because he taught that anatomy could be learnt only through dissections. He opposed and corrected the erroneous concepts of Galen and fought against his authority, thus reviving anatomy after a deadlock of about 15 centuries. His great anatomical treatise *De Febricia Humani Corporis,* written in seven volumes, revolutionized the teaching of anatomy and remained as authoritative text for two centuries.

Vesalius studied first at Louvain and then at Paris under Gunther and Sylvius. Eustachius was the rival of Vesalius. The followers of Vesalius included Servetus, Columbus, Fallopius, Varolio, Vidius, etc.; all of them lived during 16th century.

6. Seventeenth Century

William Harvey (1578–1657) was an English physician who discovered the circulation of blood, and published it as *Anatomical Exercise on the Motion of the Heart* and *Blood* in *Animals*. He also published a book on embryology.

The other events of this century included: (a) the first recorded human dissection in 1638 in Massachusetts; (b) foundation of microscopic anatomy by Malpighi; and (c) introduction of alcohol as a preservative.

7. Eighteenth Century

William Hunter (1718–1783) was a London anatomist and obstetrician. He introduced the present day embalming with the help of Harvey's discovery, and founded with his younger brother (John Hunter) the famous Hunterian museum.

8. Nineteenth Century

Dissection by medical students was made compulsory in Edinburgh (1826) and Maryland (1833). Burke and Hare scandal of 16 murders took place in Edinburgh in 1828. Warburton Anatomy Act (1932) was passed in England under which the unclaimed bodies were made available for dissection. The 'Act' was passed in America (Massachusetts) in 1831. Formalin was used as a fixative in 1890s.

X-rays were discovered by Roentgen in 1895. Various endoscopes were devised between 1819 and 1899. The anatomical societies were founded in Germany (1886), Britain (1887) and America (1888).

The noted anatomists of this century include Ashley Cooper (1768–1841; British surgeon), Cuvier (1769–1832; French naturalist), Meckel (1724–1774; German anatomist), and Henry Gray (1827–1861; the author of *Gray's Anatomy*).

9. Twentieth Century

The electron microscope was invented in 20th century. It was applied in clinical practice, which made startling changes in the study of normal and diseased conditions. Various modifications of electron microscope, transmission EM and SEM, etc. were devised. These helped in better understanding of the body tissues.

Besides plain X-rays, in this century, ultrasonography and echocardiography were discovered. This was the non-invasive safe-procedure.

Also computer-axial tomography or CT scan, a non-invasive procedure and magnetic resonance imaging were devised. These were extremely useful, sensitive means of understanding the dynamics of body structure in health and disease.

Tissue culture was developed which was new and exciting field of research.

New advances in cases of infertility were discovered, which gave hopes to some infertile couples. **GIFT:** Gamete Intrafallopian Transfer got started

10. Twenty First Century

Foetal medicine is emerging as a newer subject. Even treatment 'in-utero' is being practised in some cases.

Human genome is being prepared.

New research in drugs for many diseases, especially AIDS, is being done very enthusiastically. There is also a strong possibility of gene therapy.

Indian Anatomists

Dr. Inderjit Dewan worked chiefly on osteology and anthropology.

Dr. D.S. Choudhry did notable work on carotid body.

Dr. H. Chaterjee and Dr. H. Verma researched on embryology.

Dr. S.S. Dayal did good work in cancer biology.

Dr. Shamer Singh and his team did pioneering work on teratology.

Dr. Chaturvedi and Dr. C.D. Gupta's prominent work was on corrosion cast.

Dr. L.V. Chako, Dr. H.N. Keswani, Dr. Veena Bijlani, Dr. Gopinath, Dr. Shashi Wadhwa of All India Institute of Medical Sciences, New Delhi, researched on neuroanatomy.

Dr. Keswani and his team established museum of history of medicine.

Dr. A.K. Susheela of AIIMS, New Delhi, has done profound work on fluorosis.

Dr. M.C. Vaidya was well known for his work on leprosy and HLA.

Dr. I.B. Singh of Rohtak did enlightening studies on histology. He has been author of several books in anatomy.

Dr. A.K. Dutta of West Bengal has authored many books on anatomy.

Amongst the medical educationists are Dr. Sita Achaya, Dr. Ved Prakash, Dr. Basu, Dr. M. Kaul, Dr. Chandrama Anand, Dr. Indira Bahl, Dr. Rewa Choudhry, Dr. Smita Kakar, Dr. Anita Tuli, Dr. Shashi Raheja, Dr. Ram Prakash, Dr. Veena Bharihoke, Dr. Madhur Gupta, Dr. J.M. Kaul, Dr. Shipra Paul, Dr. Dharamnarayan, Dr. A.C. Das, Dr. A. Halim, Dr. D.R. Singh and many others.

Dr. Swarna Bhardwaj, an educationist, was appointed as Executive Director of "DNB office" and has brought the institution to forefront.

Dr. Harish Agarwal, an anatomist, worked in jurisprudence for a number of years.

Dr. Cooper of Chennai, Dr. M. Thomas and Dr. Kiran Kucheria did commendable work on genetics.

Dr. Mehdi Hasan and Dr. Nafis Ahmad Faruqi did pioneering research in neuroanatomy.

ANATOMICAL NOMENCLATURE

Galen (2nd century) wrote his book in Greek and Vesalius (16th century) did it in Latin. Most of the anatomical terms, therefore, are either in Greek or Latin. By 19th century about 30,000 anatomical terms were in use in the books and journals. In 1895, the German Anatomical Society held a meeting in Basle, and approved a list of about 5000 terms known as **Basle Nomina Anatomica** *(BNA)*. The following six rules were laid down to be followed strictly: (1) Each part shall have only one name; (2) each term shall be in Latin; (3) each term shall be as short and simple as possible; (4) the terms shall be merely memory signs; (5) the related terms shall be similar, e.g. femoral artery, femoral vein, and femoral nerve; and (6) the adjectives shall be arranged as opposites, e.g. major and minor, superior and inferior.

BNA was revised in 1933 by a committee of the Anatomical Society of Great Britain and Ireland in a meeting held at Birmingham. The revised BNA was named as **Birmingham Revision** *(BR)*. An independent revision of the BNA was also done by German anatomists in 1935, and was known as **Jena Nomina Anatomica** *(JNA* or *INA)*. However, the *BR* and *INA* found only local and restricted acceptance.

In 1950, it was agreed at an International Congress of Anatomists held at Oxford that a further attempt should be made to establish a generally acceptable international nomenclature. In the Sixth International Congress of Anatomists held at Paris (1955), a somewhat conservative revision of BNA with many terms from BR and INA was approved. Minor revisions and corrections were made at the International Congresses held in New York (1960), and Wiesbaden, Germany (1965), and the 3rd edition of **Nomina Anatomica** (Ed. G.A.G. Mitchell, 1968) was published by the Excerpta Medica Foundation.

The drafts on *Nomina Histologica* and *Nomina Embryologica* prepared by the subcommittee of the International Anatomical Nomenclature Committee (IANC) were approved in a plenary session of the Eleventh International Congress of Anatomists held in Leningrad in 1970. After a critical revision, the 4th edition of *Nomina Anatomica* (Ed. Roger Warwick, 1977) containing *Nomina Histologica* and *Nomina Embryologica* was published by the same publisher.

LANGUAGE OF ANATOMY

Various positions, planes, terms in relation to various regions and movements are described.

Positions

- **Anatomical position:** When a person is standing straight with eyes looking forwards, both arms by the side of body, palms facing forwards, both feet together, the position is anatomical position (Fig. 1.7).
- **Supine position:** When a person is lying on her/his back, arms by the side, palms facing upwards and feet put together, the position is supine position (Fig. 1.8).
- **Prone position:** Person lying on his/her face, chest and abdomen is said to be in prone position (Fig. 1.9).

Fig. 1.7: Anatomical position

Fig. 1.8: Supine position

Fig. 1.9: Prone position

- **Lithotomy position:** Person lying on her back with legs up and feet supported in straps. This position is mostly used during delivery of the baby (Fig. 1.10).

Fig. 1.10: Lithotomy position

Planes

- A plane passing through the centre of the body dividing it into two equal right and left halves, is the median or midsagittal plane (Fig.1.11). Plane parallel to median or midsagittal plane is the sagittal plane.

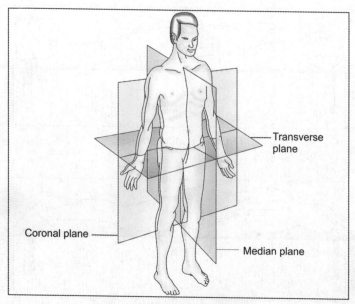

Transverse plane

Coronal plane

Median plane

Fig. 1.11: Planes of the body

- A plane at right angles to sagittal or median plane which divides the body into anterior and posterior halves is called a **coronal plane** (Fig. 1.12).
- A plane at right angles to both sagittal and coronal planes which divides the body into upper and lower parts is called a **transverse plane** (Fig.1.12).

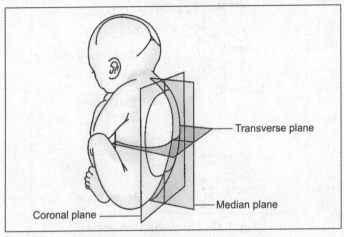

Fig. 1.12: Planes of the body in a child

Terms Used in Relation to Trunk

- **Ventral** or **Anterior** is the front of trunk.
- **Dorsal** or **Posterior** is the back of trunk (Fig. 1.13).
- **Medial** is a plane close to the median plane (Fig. 1.13).
- **Lateral** is plane away from the median plane.
- **Proximal/Cranial/Superior** is close to the head end of trunk (Fig. 1.14).
- **Distal/Caudal/Inferior** is close to the lower end of the trunk.
- **Superficial** is close to skin/towards surface of body (Fig. 1.15).
- **Deep** away from skin/away from surface of body.
- **Ipsilateral** on the same side of the body as another structure (Fig. 1.13).
- **Contralateral** on opposite side of body from another structure.
- **Invagination** is projection inside.
- **Evagination** is projection outside (Fig. 1.16).

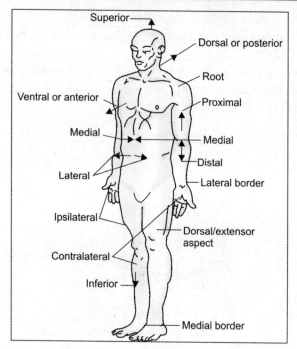

Fig. 1.13: Language of anatomy

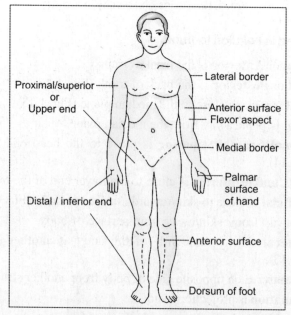

Fig. 1.14: Language of anatomy

Fig. 1.15: Language of anatomy

Invagination   Evagination

Fig. 1.16: Language of anatomy

Terms Used in Relation to Upper Limb

- **Ventral** or **Anterior** is the front aspect (Fig. 1.13).
- **Dorsal** or **Posterior** is the back aspect.
- **Medial border** lies along the little finger, medial border of forearm and arm.
- **Lateral border** follows the thumb, lateral border of forearm and arm (Fig. 1.14).
- **Proximal** is close to root of limb, while **distal** is away from the root.
- **Palmar** aspect is the front of the palm (Fig. 1.14).
- **Dorsal** aspect of hand is on the back of palm.
- **Flexor** aspect is front of upper limb.
- **Extensor** aspect is back of upper limb.

Terms Used in Relation to Lower Limb

- **Posterior** aspect is the back of lower limb.
- **Anterior** aspect is front of lower limb.
- **Medial border** lies along the big toe or hallux, medial border of leg and thigh (Fig. 1.13).

- **Lateral border** lies along the little toe, lateral border of leg and thigh.
- **Flexor** aspect is back of lower limb.
- **Extensor** aspect is front of lower limb (Fig. 1.13).
- **Proximal** is close to the root of limb, while **distal** is away from it.

Terms of Relation Commonly Used in Embryology and Comparative Anatomy, but sometimes in Gross Anatomy

(a) **Ventral** – Towards the belly (like anterior).

(b) **Dorsal** – Towards the back (like posterior).

(c) **Cranial or Rostral** – Towards the head (like superior).

(d) **Caudal** – Towards the tail.

TERMS RELATED TO BODY MOVEMENTS

Movements in general at synovial joints are divided into four main categories.

1. **Gliding movement:** Relatively flat surfaces move back-and-forth and from side-to-side with respect to one another. The angle between articulating bones does not change significantly.

2. **Angular movements:** Angle between articulating bones decreases or increases. In **flexion** there is decrease in angle between articulating bones and in **extension** there is increase in angle between articulating bones. **Lateral flexion** is movement of trunk sideways to the right or left at the waist. **Adduction** is movement of bone toward midline whereas **abduction** is movement of bone away from midline.

3. **Rotation:** A bone revolves around its own longitudinal axis. In **medial rotation** anterior surface of a bone of limb is turned towards the midline. In **lateral rotation** anterior surface of bone of limb is turned away from midline.

4. **Special movements:** These occur only at certain joints, e.g. pronation, supination at radioulnar joints, protraction and retraction at temporo-mandibular joint.

In Upper limb

- **Flexion:** When two flexor surfaces are brought close to each other, e.g. in elbow joint when front of arm and forearm are opposed to each other [Fig. 1.17 (i-v)].

- **Extension:** When extensor or dorsal surfaces are brought in as much approximation as possible, e.g. straighten the arm and forearm at the elbow joint.
- **Abduction:** When limb is taken away from the body.
- **Adduction:** When limb is brought close to the body.
- **Circumduction:** It is movement of distal end of a part of the body in a circle. A combination of extension, abduction, flexion and adduction in a sequence is called circumduction as in bowling.
- **Medial rotation:** When the arm rotates medially bringing the flexed forearm across the chest.
- **Lateral rotation:** When arm rotates laterally taking the flexed forearm away from the body.
- **Supination:** When the palm is facing forwards or upwards, as in putting food in the mouth (Fig. 1.17).
- **Pronation:** When the palm faces backwards or downwards, as in picking food with fingers from the plate.
- **Adduction of digits/fingers:** When all the fingers get together.
- **Abduction:** When all fingers separate.
The axis of movement of fingers is the line passing through the centre of the middle finger.
- **Opposition of thumb:** When tip of thumb touches the tips of any of the fingers.
- **Circumduction of thumb:** Movement of extension, abduction, flexion and adduction in sequence.

In Lower Limb

- **Flexion of thigh:** When front of thigh comes in contact with front of abdomen.
- **Extension of thigh:** When person stands erect.
- **Abduction:** When thigh is taken away from the median plane.
- **Adduction:** When thigh is brought close to median plane.
- **Medial rotation:** When thigh is turned medially.
- **Lateral rotation:** When thigh is turned laterally (Fig. 1.18).
- **Flexion of knee:** When back of thigh and back of leg come in opposition.

(i) Circumduction:
Moving in circular manner

(ii) Flexion:
Bending, decreasing the joint angle

(iii) Extension:
Straightening, increasing the joint angle

(iv) Abduction: Moving away from midline
Adduction: Moving toward midline

(v) Pronation:
Turning downward
Supination:
Turning upward

Fig. 1.17: Terms related to movements of upper limb

- **Extension of knee:** When thigh and leg are in straight line as in standing.
- **Dorsiflexion of foot:** When dorsum of foot is brought close to front of leg and sole faces forwards (Fig. 1.18).
- **Plantarflexion of foot:** When sole of foot or plantar aspect of foot faces backwards.
- **Inversion of foot:** When medial border of foot is raised from the ground (Fig. 1.18).
- **Eversion of foot:** When lateral border of foot is raised from the ground.

In the Neck

- **Flexion:** When face comes closer to chest.
- **Extension:** When face is brought away from the chest.

Fig. 1.18: Terms related to movements of lower limb

- **Lateral flexion:** When ear is brought close to shoulder.
- **Rotation:** When neck rotates so that chin goes to opposite side.
- **Opening the mouth:** When lower jaw is lowered to open the mouth.
- **Closure of the mouth:** When lower jaw is opposed to the upper jaw, closing the mouth.
- **Protraction:** When lower jaw slides forwards in its socket in the temporal bone of skull.
- **Retraction:** When lower jaw slides backwards in its socket in the temporal bone of skull (Fig. 1.19).

Fig. 1.19: Retraction and protraction at temporo-mandibular joints

In the Trunk

- Backward bending is called **extension**.
- Forward bending is **flexion** (Fig. 1.20).
- Sideward movement is **lateral flexion**.
- Sideward rotation is **lateral rotation**.

Fig. 1.20: Movements of the trunk: **(a)** extension, **(b)** flexion, **(c)** lateral flexion

Terms Used for Describing Muscles

(a) **Origin:** The end of a muscle which is relatively fixed during its contraction (Fig. 1.21).

(b) **Insertion:** The end of a muscle which moves during its contraction.

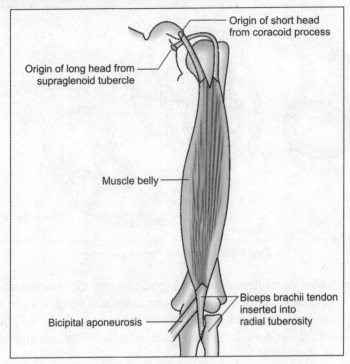

Origin of short head
from coracoid process

Origin of long head from
supraglenoid tubercle

Muscle belly

Biceps brachii tendon
inserted into
radial tuberosity

Bicipital aponeurosis

Fig. 1.21: Terms used for describing muscles

The two terms, origin and insertion, are sometimes interchangeable, when the origin moves and the insertion is fixed.

(c) **Belly:** The fleshy and contractile part of a muscle.

(d) **Tendon:** The fibrous noncontractile and cord-like part of a muscle.

(e) **Aponeurosis:** The flattened tendon.

(f) **Raphe:** A fibrous band made up of interdigitating fibres of the tendons or aponeuroses. Unlike a ligament, it is stretchable. Ligaments are fibrous, inelastic bands which connect two segments of a joint.

Terms Used for Describing Vessels

(a) **Arteries** carry oxygenated blood away from the heart, with the exception of the pulmonary and umbilical arteries which carry deoxygenated blood. Arteries resemble trees because they have branches (arterioles) (Fig. 1.22).

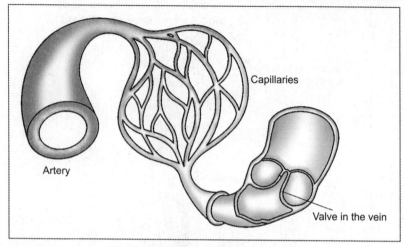

Fig. 1.22: Artery, capillaries and vein

(b) **Veins** carry deoxygenated blood towards the heart, with the exception of the pulmonary and umbilical veins which carry oxygenated blood. Veins resemble rivers because they have tributaries (venules). Veins have valves to allow unidirectional flow of blood.

(c) **Capillaries** are networks of microscopic vessels connecting arterioles to venules.

(d) **Anastomosis** is a precapillary or postcapillary communication between the neighbouring vessels (Fig. 1.23).

Terms Used for Describing Bone Features

(a) **Elevations**
1. *Linear elevation* may be a line, lip, ridge, or crest.
2. *Sharp elevation* may be a spine, styloid process, cornu (horn), or hamulus (Fig. 1.24).
3. *Rounded* or *irregular elevation* may be a tubercle, tuberosity, epicondyle, malleolus, or trochanter. A ramus is a broad arm or process projecting from the main part or body of the bone (Figs 1.25–1.27).

(b) **Depressions** may be a pit, impression, fovea, fossa, groove (sulcus), or notch (incisura).

(c) **Openings** may be a foramen, canal, hiatus, or aqueduct.

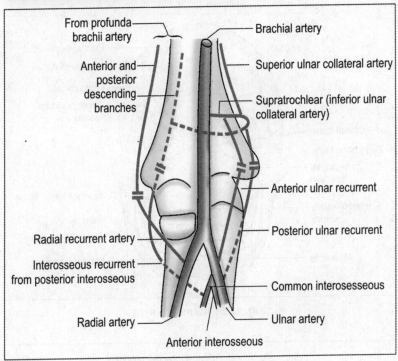

Fig. 1.23: Anastomoses around elbow joint

Fig. 1.24: Norma basalis

Fig. 1.25: Norma frontalis

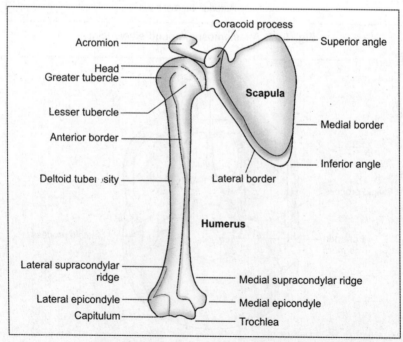

Fig. 1.26: Right scapula and humerus (anterior view)

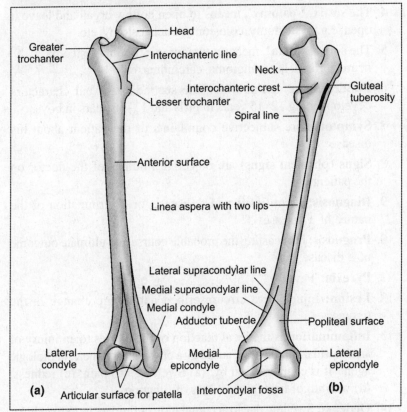

Head
Greater trochanter
Interochanteric line
Neck
Interochanteric crest
Lesser trochanter
Gluteal tuberosity
Spiral line
Anterior surface
Linea aspera with two lips
Lateral supracondylar line
Medial supracondylar line
Medial condyle
Adductor tubercle
Popliteal surface
Lateral condyle
Medial epicondyle
Lateral epicondyle
(a)
Articular surface for patella
Intercondylar fossa
(b)

Fig. 1.27 Femur—anterior surface **(a)** and posterior surface **(b)**

(d) **Cavities:** A large cavity within a bone is called sinus, cell or antrum.

(e) **Smooth articular areas** may be a facet, condyle, head, capitulum, or trochlea.

Terms Used in Clinical Anatomy

1. The suffix, **'-itis'**, means inflammation, e.g. appendicitis, tonsillitis, arthritis, neuritis, dermatitis, etc.

2. The suffix, **'-ectomy'**, means removal from the body, e.g. appendicectomy, tonsillectomy, gastrectomy, nephrectomy, etc.

3. The suffix, **'-otomy'**, means to open and then close a hollow organ, e.g. laparotomy, hysterotomy, cystotomy, cystolithotomy, etc.

4. The suffix, **'-ostomy'**, means to open hollow organ and leave it open, e.g. cystostomy, colostomy, tracheostomy, etc.

5. The suffix, **'-oma'**, means a tumour, e.g. lipoma, osteoma, neurofibroma, haemangioma, carcinoma, etc.

6. **Puberty:** The age at which the secondary sexual characters develop, being 12–15 years in girls and 13–16 years in boys.

7. **Symptoms** are subjective complaints of the patient about his disease.

8. **Signs (physical signs)** are objective findings of the doctor on the patient.

9. **Diagnosis:** Identification of a disease, or determination of the nature of a disease.

10. **Prognosis:** Forecasting the probable course and ultimate outcome of a disease.

11. **Pyrexia:** Fever.

12. **Lesion:** Injury, or a circumscribed pathologic change in the tissues.

13. **Inflammation** is the local reaction of the tissues to an injury or an abnormal stimulation caused by a physical, chemical, or biologic agent. It is characterized by: (a) Swelling; (b) pain; (c) redness; (d) warmth of heat; and (e) loss of function.

14. **Oedema:** Swelling due to accumulation of fluid in the extracellular space.

15. **Thrombosis:** Intravascular coagulation (solidification) of blood.

16. **Embolism:** Occlusion of a vessel by a detached and circulating thrombus (embolus).

17. **Haemorrhage:** Bleeding which may be external or internal.

18. **Ulcer:** A localized breach (gap, erosion) in the surface continuity of the skin or mucous membrane.

19. **Sinus:** A blind track (open at one end) lined by epithelium.

20. **Fistula:** A track open at both the ends and lined by epithelium.

21. **Necrosis:** Local death of a tissue or organ due to irreversible damage to the nucleus.

22. **Degeneration:** A retrogressive change causing deterioration in the structural and functional qualities. It is a reversible process, but may end in necrosis.

23. **Gangrene:** A form of necrosis (death) combined with putrefaction.
24. **Infarction:** Death (necrosis) of a tissue due to sudden obstruction of its artery of supply (often an end-artery).
25. **Atrophy:** Diminution in the size of cells, tissue, organ, or a part due to loss of its nutrition.
26. **Dystrophy:** Diminution in the size due to defective nutrition.
27. **Hypertrophy:** Increase in the size without any increase in the number of cells.
28. **Hyperplasia:** Increase in the size due to increase in the number of cells.
29. **Hypoplasia:** Incomplete development.
30. **Aplasia:** Failure of development.
31. **Syndrome:** A group of diverse symptoms and signs constituting together the picture of a disease.
32. **Paralysis:** Loss of motor power (movement) of a part of body due to denervation or primary disease of the muscles.
33. **Hemiplegia:** Paralysis of one-half of the body.
34. **Paraplegia:** Paralysis of both the lower limbs.
35. **Monoplegia:** Paralysis of any one limb.
36. **Quadriplegia:** Paralysis of all the four limbs.
37. **Anaesthesia:** Loss of the touch sensibility.
38. **Analgesia:** Loss of the pain sensibility.
39. **Thermanaesthesia:** Loss of the temperature sensibility.
40. **Hyperaesthesia:** Abnormally increased sensibility.
41. **Paraesthesia:** Perverted feeling of sensations.
42. **Coma:** Deep unconsciousness.
43. **Tumour (neoplasm):** A circumscribed, noninflammatory, abnormal growth arising from the body tissues.
44. **Benign:** Mild illness or growth which does not endanger life.
45. **Malignant:** Severe form of illness or growth, which is resistant to treatment and ends in death.
46. **Carcinoma:** Malignant growth arising from the epithelium (ectoderm or endoderm).
47. **Sarcoma:** Malignant growth arising from connective tissue (mesoderm).

48. **Cancer:** A general term used to indicate any malignant neoplasm which shows invasiveness and results in death of the patient.
49. **Metastasis:** Spread of a local disease (like the cancer cells) to distant parts of the body.
50. **Convalescence:** The recovery period between the end of a disease and restoration to complete health.
51. **Therapy:** Medical treatment.

ARRANGEMENT OF STRUCTURES IN THE BODY FROM WITHIN OUTWARDS

1. Bones form the supporting framework of the body.
2. Muscles are attached to bones.
3. Blood vessels, nerves and lymphatics form neurovascular bundles which course in between the muscles, along the fascial planes.
4. The thoracic and abdominal cavities contain several internal organs called viscera.
5. The whole body has three general coverings, namely (a) skin; (b) superficial fascia; and (c) deep fascia.

2

Skeleton

Skeleton includes bones and cartilages. It forms the main supporting framework of the body, and is primarily designed for a more effective production of movements by the attached muscles.

BONES

Synonyms

1. Os (L),
2. Osteon (G).

Compare with the terms, osteology, ossification, osteomyelitis, osteomalacia, osteoma, osteotomy, etc.

Definition

Bone is one-third connective tissue. It is impregnated with calcium salts which constitute two-thirds part. The inorganic calcium salts (mainly calcium phosphate, partly calcium carbonate, and traces of other salts) make it hard and rigid, which can afford resistance to compressive forces of weight-bearing and impact forces of jumping. The organic connective tissue (collagen fibres) makes it tough and resilient (flexible), which can afford resistance to tensile forces. In strength, bone is comparable to iron and steel.

Despite its hardness and high calcium content the bone is very much a living tissue. It is highly vascular, with a constant turn-over of its calcium content. It shows a characteristic pattern of growth. It is subjected to disease and heals after a fracture. It has greater regenerative power than any other tissue of the body, except blood. It can mould itself according to changes in stress and strain it bears. It shows disuse atrophy and overuse hypertrophy.

Divisions of the Skeletal System (Fig. 2.1)		
Regions of the Skeleton	**Number of Bones**	**Cranial and facial bones: (mnemonic is A–Z)**
AXIAL SKELETON		
Skull		
Cranium	8	**A–D** –
Face	14	Ethmoid 1
Hyoid	1	Frontal 1
Auditory ossicles (3 in each ear):	6	**G–H** –
(Malleus, incus, stapes)		Inferior nasal
Vertebral column	26	choncha 2
Thorax		**J–K** –
Sternum	1	Lacrimal 2
Ribs	24	Maxilla 2
APPENDICULAR SKELETON		Mandible 1
Pectoral (shoulder) girdles		Nasal 2
Clavicle	2	Occipital 1
Scapula	2	Parietal 2
Upper extremities		Palatine 2
Humerus	2	**Q–R** –
Ulna	2	Sphenoid 1
Radius	2	Temporal 2
Carpals	16	**U** –
Metacarpals	10	Vomer 1
Phalanges	28	**W–Y** –
Pelvic (hip) girdle		Zygomatic 2
Pelvic, or hip bone	2	
Lower extremities		
Femur	2	
Fibula	2	
Tibia	2	
Patella	2	
Tarsals	14	
Metatarsals	10	
Phalanges	28	
	126	
Total	**206**	

Functions

1. Bones give shape and support to the body, and resist any forms of stress (Fig. 2.1).
2. These provide surface for the attachment of muscles, tendons, ligaments, etc.
3. These serve as levers for muscular actions.
4. The skull, vertebral column and thoracic cage protect brain, spinal cord and thoracic viscera, respectively.
5. Bone marrow manufactures blood cells.
6. Bones store 97% of the body calcium and phosphorus.
7. Bone marrow contains reticulo-endothelial cells which are phagocytic in nature and take part in immune responses of the body.
8. The larger paranasal air sinuses affect the timber of the voice.

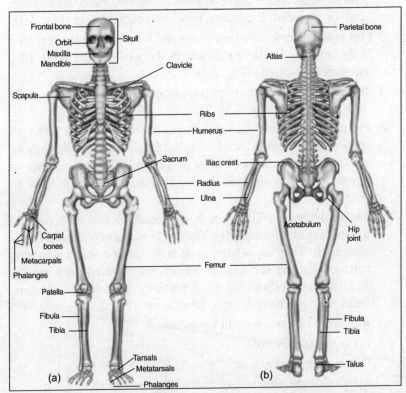

Fig. 2.1: Human skeleton: **(a)** Anterior view, **(b)** Posterior view

CLASSIFICATION OF BONES

A. According to Shape

1. **Long bones:** Each long bone has an elongated shaft (diaphysis) and two expanded ends (epiphyses) which are smooth and articular. The shaft typically has 3 surfaces separated by 3 borders, a central medullary cavity, and a nutrient foramen directed away from the growing end. Examples:

   (a) typical long bones like humerus, radius, ulna, femur, tibia and fibula;

   (b) miniature long bones have only one epiphysis like metacarpals, metatarsals and phalanges; and

   (c) modified long bones have no medullary cavity like clavicle (Fig. 2.2).

2. **Short bones:** Their shape is usually cuboid, cuneiform, trapezoid, or scaphoid. Examples: tarsal and carpal bones (Fig. 2.3).

3. **Flat bones** resemble shallow plates and form boundaries of certain body cavities. Examples: bones in the vault of the skull, ribs, sternum and scapula (Fig. 2.4).

4. **Irregular bones:** Examples: vertebra, hip bone, and bones in the base of the skull (Fig. 2.5).

5. **Pneumatic bones:** Certain irregular bones contain large air spaces lined by epithelium Examples: maxilla, sphenoid, ethmoid, etc. They make the skull light in weight, help in resonance of voice, and act as air conditioning chambers for the inspired air (Fig. 2.6).

6. **Sesamoid bones:** These are bony nodules found embedded in the tendons or joint capsules. They have no periosteum and ossify after birth. They are related to an articular or nonarticular bony surface, and the surfaces of contact are covered with hyaline cartilage and lubricated by a bursa or synovial membrane. Examples: patella, pisiform, fabella, etc. (Fig. 2.7).

   Functions of the sesamoid bones are:

   (a) to resist pressure;

   (b) to minimise friction;

   (c) to alter the direction of pull of the muscle; and

   (d) to maintain the local circulation.

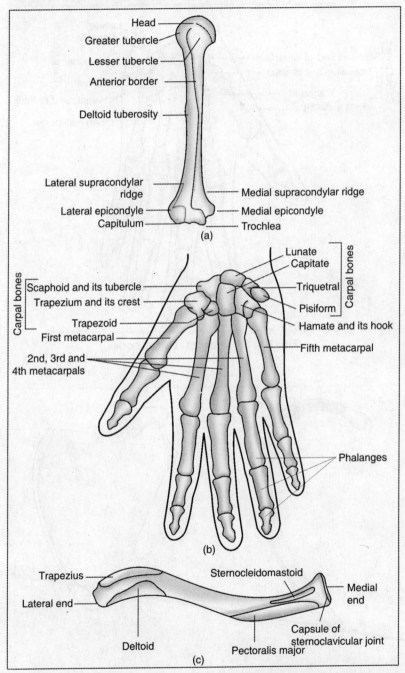

Fig. 2.2: Long bones: **(a)** Humerus, **(b)** Metacarpals, **(c)** Clavicle

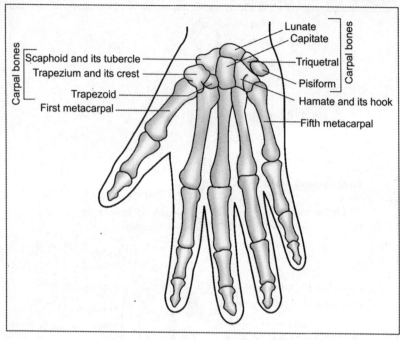

Fig. 2.3: Small bones: Carpal bones

Fig. 2.4: Flat bones: **(a)** Rib, **(b)** Scapula

Fig. 2.5: Irregular bones: Vertebrae **(a)** 1st cervical, **(b)** 2nd cervical

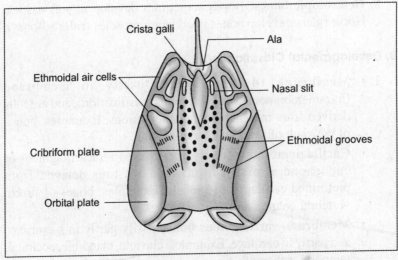

Fig. 2.6: Pneumatic bone: Ethmoid

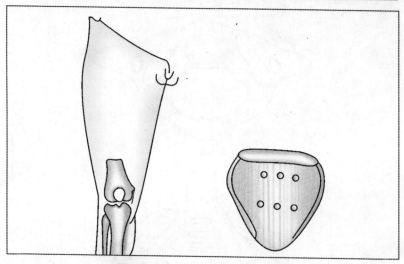

Fig. 2.7: Sesamoid bone: Patella

7. **Accessory (supernumerary) bones** are not always present. These may occur as ununited epiphyses developed from extra centres of ossification. Examples: sutural bones, os trigonum (lateral tubercle of talus), os vesalianum (tuberosity of 5th metatarsal), etc. In medicolegal practice, accessory bones may be mistaken for fractures. However, these are often bilateral, and have smooth surfaces without any callus.

8. **Heterotopic bones:** Bones sometimes develop in soft tissues. Horse riders develop bones in adductor muscles (rider's bones).

B. Developmental Classification

1. • **Membrane (dermal) bones** ossify in membrane (intramembranous or mesenchymal ossification), and are thus derived from mesenchymal condensations. Examples: bones of the vault of skull and facial bones.

   • **Cartilaginous bones** ossify in cartilage (intracartilaginous or endochondral ossification), and are thus derived from preformed cartilaginous models. Examples: bones of limbs, vertebral column and thoracic cage.

   • **Membrano-cartilaginous bones** ossify partly in membrane and partly in cartilage. Examples: clavicle, mandible, occipital, temporal, sphenoid.

2. • **Somatic bones:** Most of the bones are somatic.
   • **Visceral bones:** These develop from pharyngeal arches. Examples are hyoid bones, part of mandible and ear ossicles.

C. Regional Classification

1. Axial skeleton includes skull, vertebral column, and thoracic cage.
2. Appendicular skeleton includes bones of the limbs.

D. Structural Classification

I. *Macroscopically,* the architecture of bone may be compact or cancellous (Fig. 2.8).

1. Compact bone is dense in texture like ivory, but is extremely porous. It is best developed in the cortex of the long bones. This is an adaptation to bending and twisting forces (a combination of compression, tension and shear).

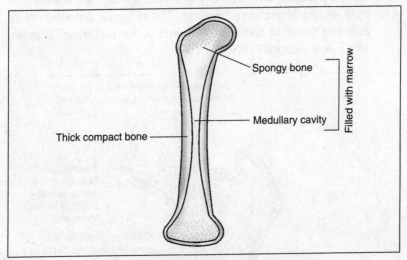

Spongy bone

Medullary cavity

Filled with marrow

Thick compact bone

Fig. 2.8: Structural components of a bone

2. Cancellous or spongy, or trabecular bone is open in texture, and is made up of a meshwork of trabeculae (rods and plates) between which are marrow containing spaces. The trabecular meshworks are of three primary types, namely:

(a) meshwork of rods,

(b) meshwork of rods and plates, and

(c) meshwork of plates (Singh, 1978).

Cancellous bone is an adaptation to compressive forces.

Bones are marvellously constructed to combine strength, elasticity and lightness in weight. Though the architecture of bone may be modified by mechanical forces, the form of the bone is primarily determined by heredity.

According to *Wolff's law* (Trajectory Theory of Wolff, 1892), the bone formation is directly proportional to stress and strain. There are two forces, tensile force and compressive force. Both the tensile and compressive forces can stimulate bone formation in proper conditions.

The architecture of cancellous bone is often interpreted in terms of the trajectorial theory. Thus the arrangement of bony trabeculae (lamellae) is governed by the lines of maximal internal stress in the bone. *Pressure lamellae* are arranged parallel to the line of weight transmission, whereas *tension lamellae* are arranged at right angles to pressure lamellae. The compact arrangement of pressure lamellae forms bony buttress, for additional support, like calcar femorale (Fig. 2.9).

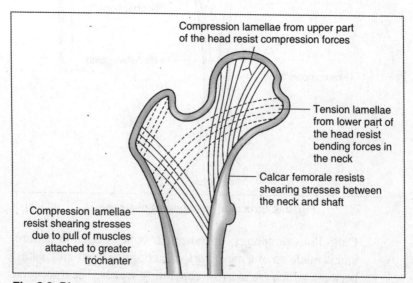

Fig. 2.9: Diagrammatic representation of the compression (continuous lines) and tension (interrupted lines) lamellae in a sagittal section of the upper end of right femur.

II. *Microscopically,* the bone is of five types, namely lamellar (including both compact and cancellous), woven, fibrous, dentine and cement.

1. **Lamellar bone:** Most of the mature human bones, whether compact or cancellous, are composed of thin plates of bony tissue called lamellae. These are arranged in piles in a cancellous bone, but in concentric cylinders (Haversian system or secondary osteon) in a compact bone.

2. **Woven Bone:** seen in fetal bone, fracture repair and in cancer of bone

3. **Fibrous bone** is found in young foetal bones, but are common in reptiles and amphibia.

4. **Dentine** and

5. **Cement** occur in teeth.

Table 2.1: Comparison of compact and cancellous bones

	Compact bone	Cancellous (spongy) bone
Location	In shaft (diaphysis) of long bone	In the epiphyses of long bone
Lamellae	Arranged to form Haversian system	Arranged in a meshwork, so Haversion systems are not present
Bone marrow	Yellow which stores fat after puberty. It is red before puberty	Red, produce RBCs, granular series of WBC and platelets
Nature	Hard and ivory like	Spongy

GROSS STRUCTURE OF AN ADULT LONG BONE

Naked eye examination of the longitudinal and transverse sections of a long bone shows the following features.

1. **Shaft:** From without inwards, it is composed of periosteum, cortex and medullary cavity (Fig. 2.10).

   (a) *Periosteum* is a thick fibrous membrane covering the surface of the bone. It is made up of an outer fibrous layer, and an inner cellular layer which is osteogenic in nature. Periosteum is united to the underlying bone by Sharpey's fibres, and the union is particularly strong over the attachments of tendons, and ligaments. At the articular margin the periosteum is continuous with the capsule of the joint. The abundant periosteal arteries nourish the outer part of the underlying cortex also. Periosteum has a rich nerve supply which makes it the most sensitive part of the bone.

(b) *Cortex* is made up of a compact bone which gives it the desired strength to withstand all possible mechanical strains.

(c) *Medullary cavity* is filled with red or yellow bone marrow. At birth the marrow is red everywhere with widespread active haemopoiesis. As the age advances, the red marrow at many places atrophies and is replaced by yellow, fatty marrow, with no power of haemopoiesis. Red marrow persists in the cancellous ends of long bones. In the sternum ribs, iliac crest, vertebrae and skull bones the red marrow is found throughout life.

2. The **two ends** of a long bone are made up of cancellous bone covered with hyaline (articular) cartilage (Fig. 2.10).

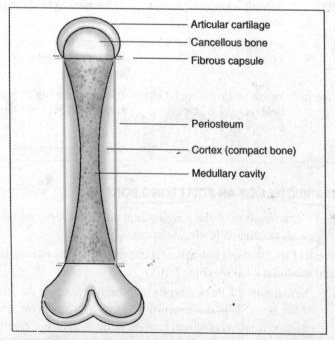

Fig. 2.10: Naked eye structure of an adult long bone in longitudinal section

PARTS OF A YOUNG BONE

A typical long bone ossifies in three parts, the two ends from secondary centres, and the intervening shaft from a primary centre (Fig. 2.11). Before ossification is complete the following parts of the bone can be defined.

Fig. 2.11: Parts of a young long bone.

1. **Epiphysis** *2⁰ ossification centre*

The ends and tips of a bone which ossify from secondary centres are called epiphyses. These are of the following types.

(a) Pressure epiphysis is articular and takes part in transmission of the weight. Examples: head of femur; lower end of radius, etc. (Fig. 2.12)

(b) Traction epiphysis is nonarticular and does not take part in the transmission of the weight. It always provides attachment to one or more tendons which exert a traction on the epiphysis. The traction epiphyses ossify later than the pressure epiphyses. Examples: trochanters of femur and tubercles of humerus (Figs 1.26 and 1.27).

(c) Atavistic epiphysis is phylogenetically an independent bone which in man becomes fused to another bone.

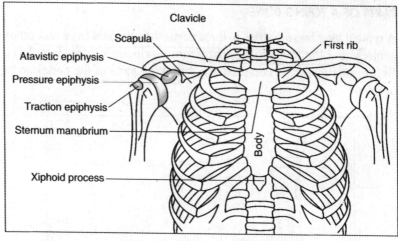

Fig. 2.12: Types of epiphyses

Examples: coracoid process of scapula and os trigonum or lateral tubercle of talus.

(d) Aberrant epiphysis is not always present. Examples: epiphysis at the head of the first metacarpal and at the base of other metacarpal bones.

2. Diaphysis

It is the elongated shaft of a long bone which ossifies from a primary centre (Fig. 2.11).

3. Metaphysis

The epiphysial ends of a diaphysis are called metaphyses.

Each metaphysis is the zone of active growth. Before epiphysial fusion, the metaphysis is richly supplied with blood through end arteries forming 'hair-pin' bends.

This is the common site of osteomyelitis in children because the bacteria or emboli are easily trapped in the hair-pin bends, causing infarction.

After the epiphysial fusion, vascular communications are established between the metaphysial and epiphysial arteries. Now the metaphysis contains no more end-arteries and is no longer subjected to osteomyelitis.

4. Epiphysial Plate of Cartilage

It separates epiphysis from metaphysis.

Proliferation of cells in this cartilaginous plate is responsible for lengthwise growth of a long bone.

After the epiphysial fusion, the bone can no longer grow in length.

The growth cartilage is nourished by both the epiphysial and metaphysial arteries.

BLOOD SUPPLY OF BONES

1. Long Bones

The blood supply of a long bone is derived from the following sources (Fig. 2.13).

(a) **Nutrient artery**
   - It enters the shaft through the nutrient foramen, runs obliquely through the cortex, and divides into ascending and descending branches in the medullary cavity.

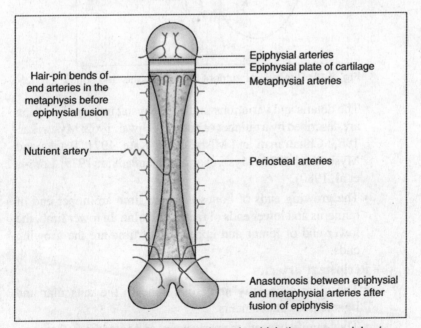

Hair-pin bends of end arteries in the metaphysis before epiphysial fusion

Nutrient artery

Epiphysial arteries
Epiphysial plate of cartilage
Metaphysial arteries

Periosteal arteries

Anastomosis between epiphysial and metaphysial arteries after fusion of epiphysis

Fig. 2.13: Blood supply of a long bone in which the upper epiphysis (growing end) has not yet fused with the diaphysis.

- Each branch divides into a number of small parallel channels which terminate in the adult metaphysis by anastomosing with the epiphysial, metaphysial and periosteal arteries.
- The nutrient artery supplies medullary cavity, inner 2/3 of cortex and metaphysis.
- The *nutrient foramen* is directed away from the growing end of the bone; their directions are indicated by a jingle, 'To the elbow I go, from the knee I flee' (Fig. 2.14).

Fig. 2.14: Direction of nutrient foramen in the limb bones

- The details and variations in the diaphysial nutrient foramina are described by a number of authors (Ujwal, 1962; Mysorekar, 1967; Chhatrapati and Misra, 1967; Kate, 1971; Patake and Mysorekar, 1977; Mysorekar and Nandedkar, 1979; Longia et al, 1980).
- The growing ends of bones in upper limb are upper end of humerus and lower ends of radius and ulna. In lower limb, the lower end of femur and upper end of tibia are the growing ends.

(b) **Periosteal arteries**
- These are especially numerous beneath the muscular and ligamentous attachments.
- They ramify beneath the periosteum and enter the Volkmann's canals to supply the outer 1/3 of the cortex.

(c) Epiphysial arteries

- These are derived from periarticular vascular arcades (circulus vasculosus) found on the nonarticular bony surface.
- Out of the numerous vascular foramina in this region, only a few admit the arteries (epiphysial and metaphysial), and the rest are venous exits.
- The number and size of these foramina may give an idea of the relative vascularity of the two ends of a long bone (Tandon, 1964).

(d) Metaphysial arteries

- These are derived from the neighbouring systemic vessels.
- They pass directly into the metaphysis and reinforce the metaphysial branches from the primary nutrient artery.

In miniature long bones, the infection begins in the middle of the shaft rather than at the metaphysis because, the nutrient artery breaks up into a plexus immediately upon reaching the medullary cavity. In the adults, however, the chances of infection are minimized because the nutrient artery is mostly replaced by the periosteal vessels.

2. Other Bones

Short bones are supplied by numerous periosteal vessels which enter their nonarticular surfaces.

In a vertebra, the body is supplied by anterior and posterior vessels; and the vertebral arch by large vessels entering the bases of transverse processes. Its marrow is drained by two large basivertebral veins.

A rib is supplied by : (a) the nutrient artery which enters it just beyond the tubercle; and (b) the periosteal arteries.

Veins are numerous and large in the cancellous, red marrow containing bones (e.g., basivertebral veins). In the compact bone, they accompany arteries in the Volkmann's canals.

Lymphatics have not been demonstrated within the bone, although some of them do accompany the periosteal blood vessels, which drain to the regional lymph nodes.

NERVE SUPPLY OF BONES

Nerves accompany the blood vessels. Most of them are sympathetic and vasomotor in function.

A few of them are sensory which are distributed to the articular ends and periosteum of the long bones, to the vertebra, and to large flat bones.

DEVELOPMENT AND OSSIFICATION OF BONES

Bones are first laid down as mesodermal (connective tissue) condensations. Conversion of mesodermal models into bone is called *intramembranous* or *mesenchymal ossification,* and the bones are called membrane (dermal) bones.

However, mesodermal stage may pass through cartilaginous stage by chondrification during 2nd month of intrauterine life. Conversion of cartilaginous model into bone is called *intracartilaginous* or *endochondral ossification,* and such bones are called cartilaginous bones (Fig. 2.15).

Ossification takes place by centres of ossification, each one of which is a point where laying down of lamellae (bone formation) starts by the osteoblasts situated on the newly formed capillary loops. The centres of ossification may be primary or secondary. The *primary centres* appear before birth, usually during 8th week of intrauterine life; the *secondary centres* appear after birth, with a few exceptions of lower end of femur and upper end of tibia. Many secondary centres appear during puberty.

A primary centre forms diaphysis, and the secondary centres form epiphyses. Fusion of epiphyses with the diaphysis starts at puberty and is complete by the age of 25 years, after which no more bone growth can take place. The *law of ossification* states that secondary centres of ossification which appear first are last to unite. The end of a long bone where epiphysial fusion is delayed is called the *growing end of the bone.*

GROWTH OF A LONG BONE

1. Bone grows in length by multiplication of cells in the epiphysial plate of cartilage (Fig. 2.15).
2. Bone grows in thickness by multiplication of cells in the deeper layer of periosteum.
3. Bones grow by deposition of new bone on the surface and at the ends. This process of bone deposition by osteoblasts is called *appositional growth* or surface accretion. However, in order to maintain the shape the unwanted bone must be removed. This

process of bone removal by osteoblasts is called *remodelling*. This is how marrow cavity increases in size.

Fig. 2.15: Growth of a long bone

MEDICOLEGAL AND ANTHROPOLOGICAL ASPECTS

When a skeleton or isolated bones are received for medicolegal examination, one should be able to determine:

(a) whether the bones are human or not;

(b) whether they belong to one or more persons;

(c) the age of the individual;

(d) the sex;

(e) the stature; and

(f) the time and cause of death.

For excellent details of all these points consult Modi (1977).

1. Estimation of Skeletal Age

Up to the age of 25 years, the skeletal age can be estimated to within 1–2 years of correct age by the states of dentition and ossification, provided the whole skeleton is available.

From 25 years onwards, the skeletal age can be estimated to within ± 5 years of the correct age by the state of cranial sutures and of the bony surfaces of symphysis pubis.

In general, the appearance of secondary centres and fusion of epiphyses occur about one year earlier in females than in males.

These events are also believed to occur 1-2 years (Bajaj et al, 1967) or 2–3 years (Pillai, 1936) earlier in India than in Western countries.

However, Jit and Singh (1971) did not find any difference between the eastern and western races.

2. Estimation of Sex

Sex can be determined after the age of puberty.

Sexual differences are best marked in the pelvis and skull, and accurate determination of sex can be done in over 90% cases with either pelvis or skull alone.

However, sexual dimorphism has been worked out in a number of other bones, like sternum (Jit et al, 1980), atlas (Halim and Siddiqui, 1976), and most of the limb bones.

3. Estimation of Stature (Height)

It is a common experience that trunk and limbs show characteristic ratios among themselves and in comparison with total height.

Thus a number of regression formulae have been worked out to determine height from the length of the individual limb bones (Siddiqui and Shah, 1944; Singh and Sohal, 1952; Jit and Singh, 1956; Athawale, 1963; Kolte and Bansal, 1974; Kate and Majumdar, 1976).

Height can also be determined from parts of certain long bones (Mysorekar et al), from head length (Saxena et al, 1981), and from foot measurements (Charnalia, 1961; Qamra et al, 1980).

CR length has been correlated with diaphysial length of foetal bones (Vare and Bansal, 1977) and with the neonatal and placental parameters (Jeyasingh et al, 1980; Saxena et al, 1981).

4. Estimation of Race

It is of interest to anthropologists. A number of metrical (like cranial and facial indices) and non metrical features of the skull, pelvis, and certain other bones are of racial significance (Krogman, 1962; Berry, 1975).

CARTILAGE

Synonyms

1. Chondros (G); 2. Gristle. Compare with the terms chondrification, chondrodystrophy, synchondrosis, etc.

Definition

Cartilage is a connective tissue composed of cells (chondrocytes) and fibres (collagen or yellow elastic) embedded in a firm, gel-like matrix which is rich in a mucopolysaccharide. It is much more elastic than bone.

General Features

1. Cartilage has no blood vessels or lymphatics. The nutrition of cells diffuses through the matrix.
2. Cartilage has no nerves. It is, therefore, insensitive.
3. Cartilage is surrounded by a fibrous membrane, called perichondrium, which is similar to periosteum in structure and function. The articular cartilage has no perichondrium, so that its regeneration after injury is inadequate.
4. When cartilage calcifies, the chondrocytes die and the cartilage is replaced by bone like tissue.

Table 2.2 shows the comparison between bone and cartilage.

Table 2.2: Comparison between bone and cartilage	
Bone	**Cartilage**
1. Bone is hard	Cartilage is firm
2. Matrix has inflexible material called ossein	It has chondroitin providing flexibility
3. Matrix possesses calcium salt	Calcium salts not present
4. Bone has rich nerve supply. It is vascular in nature	It does not have nerve supply. It is avascular in nature
5. Bone marrow is present	Bone marrow is absent
6. Growth is only by apposition (by surface deposition)	Growth is appositional and interstitial (from within)

Types of Cartilage

There are three types of cartilages:

1. Hyaline cartilage (Fig. 2.16)
2. Fibrocartilage (Fig. 2.17)
3. Elastic cartilage (Fig. 2.16)

Table 2.3 reveals the comparison between three types of cartilages.

	Hyaline Cartilage	**Fibrocartilage**	**Elastic cartilage**
Table 2.3: Comparison of three types of cartilages			
Location	In the articular cartilages of long bones, sternum, ribs, nasal and some laryngeal cartilages	In the intervertebral disc of pubic symphysis, temporomandibular joints, sterno-clavicular joint	In the pinna, external auditory meatus, Eustachian tubes, epiglottis, vocal process of arytenoid cartilage
Colour	Bluish white	Glistening white	Yellowish
Appearance	Shiny or translucent	Opaque	Opaque
Fibres	Very thin, having same refractive index as matrix, so these are not seen	Numerous white fibres	Numerous yellow fibres
Elasticity	Flexible	More firm strongest	Most flexible

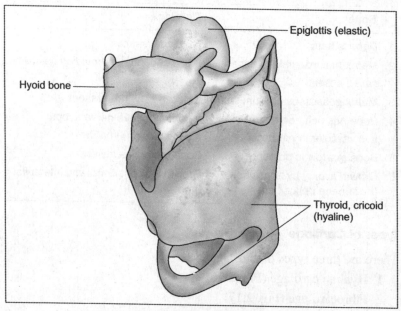

Fig. 2.16: Hyaline and elastic cartilages

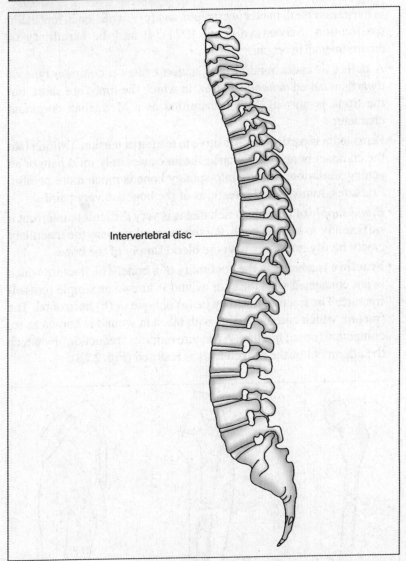

Intervertebral disc

Fig. 2.17: Fibrocartilage: Intervertebral disc

CLINICAL ANATOMY

- A defect in membranous ossification causes a rare syndrome called *cleidocranial dysostosis*. It is characterized by three cardinal features: (a) Varying degrees of aplasia of the clavicles; (b) increase in the transverse diameter of cranium, and (c) retardation in fontanelle ossification (Srivastava et al, 1971). It may be hereditary or environmental in origin.

• A defect in endochondral ossification causes a common type of dwarfism called *achondroplasia*, in which the limbs are short, but the trunk is normal. It is transmitted as a Mendelian dominant character.

• Periosteum is particularly sensitive to tearing or tension. Drilling into the compact bone without anaesthesia causes only mild pain or an aching sensation; drilling into spongy bone is much more painful. Fractures, tumours and infections of the bone are very painful.

• *Blood supply* of bone is so rich that it is very difficult to interrupt it sufficiently to kill the bone. Passing a metal pin into the medullary cavity hardly interferes with the blood supply of the bone.

• **Fracture** is a break in the continuity of a bone. The fracture which is not connected with the skin wound is known as simple (closed) fracture. The fracture line may be (a) oblique or (b) horizontal. The fracture which communicates with the skin wound is known as (c) compound (open) fracture. A fracture requires "reduction" by which the alignment of the broken ends is restored (Fig. 2.18).

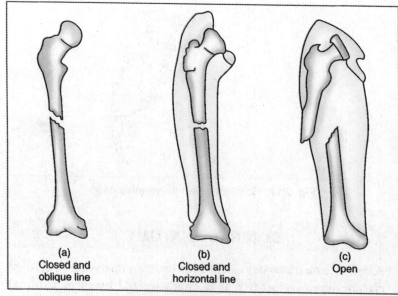

| (a) | (b) | (c) |
| Closed and oblique line | Closed and horizontal line | Open |

Fig. 2.18: Types of fractures

Healing (repair) of a fracture takes place in three stages:

(a) Repair by granulation tissue;

(b) union by callus; and

(c) consolidation by mature bone.

- Axis or 2nd cervical vertebra may get fractured. If dens of axis gets separated from the body, it hits the vital centres in the medulla oblongata causing instantaneous death (Fig. 2.19). Even fracture of laminae may cause death.

Fig. 2.19: "Hanging till death" occurs due to fracture of dens of axis vertebra

- In **rickets** (deficiency of vitamin D), calcification of cartilage fails and ossification of the growth zone is disturbed. Rickets affects the growing bones and, therefore, the disease develops during the period of most rapid growth of skeleton, i.e. 3 months to 3 years. Osteoid tissue is formed normally and the cartilage cells proliferate freely, but mineralization does not take place. This results in craniotabes, rachitic rosary at the costochondral junctions, Harrison's sulcus at the diaphragmatic attachments, enlarged epiphyses in limb bones (Fig. 2.20) and the spinal and pelvic deformities.

- For proper development of bones, a child requires adequate amounts of proteins, calcium, vitamin D, etc. Deficiency of calcium and vitamin D in growing children leads to widening of ends of bones with inadequate ossification. This condition is called as rickets (Fig. 2.20).

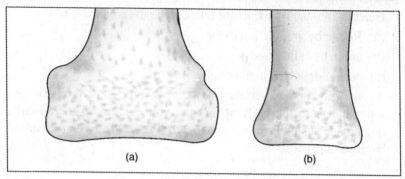

Fig. 2.20: (a) Rickets, **(b)** Normal

- In scurvy (deficiency of vitamin C), formation of collagenous fibres and matrix is impaired. Defective formation of the intercellular cementing substances and lack of collagen cause rupture of capillaries and defective formation of new capillaries. Haematoma in the muscles and bones (subperiosteal) cause severe pain and tenderness. The normal architecture at the growing ends of the bones is lost.

- Many skeletal defects are caused by genetic factors, or by a combination of genetic, hormonal, nutritional and pathological factors.

- The vertebral arch or laminae of the vertebral column may remain deficient, the spinal cord may be covered by skin, i.e. (a) spina bifida occulta. There may be protrusion of the meninges surrounding the spinal cord placed in the vertebral canal, i.e. (b) meningocele or there may be protrusion of the spinal cord as well as meninges, i.e. (c) meningo-myelocele (Fig. 2.21).

Fig. 2.21: Types of spina bifida: **(a)** Spina bifida occulta, **(b)** Meningocele, **(c)** meningo-myelocele

- If deficiency of calcium, vitamin D occurs in adult life, it leads *osteomalacia*. The bones on X-rays examination do not reveal enough trabeculae.

Deficiency of calcium in bones in old age leads to *osteoporosis*, seen both in females and males. Due to osteoporosis, there is forward bending of the vertebral column, leading to kyphosis (Fig. 2.22).

- Nerves are closely related to bones in some areas. Fracture of the bones of those areas may lead to injury to the nerve, leading to paralysis of muscles supplied including the sensory loss (Fig. 2.23).

Fig. 2.22: Kyphosis due to osteoporosis

Fig. 2.23: Nerves in contact with posterior surface of humerus

Table 2.4: Comparison of osteoporosis and osteomalacia				
	Calcium & phosphate	Alkaline phosphatase	Osteo-blast	Trabeculae
Osteoporosis	Normal	Normal	Normal	Thin and small
Osteomalacia	May be low	Raised	Increased	Thick uncalcified osteoid

- **Bone marrow biopsy:** Bone marrow can be taken either from manubrium sterni or iliac crest in various clinical conditions (Fig. 2.24).
- **Bone tumour:** Benign or malignant tumours can occur in the bone (Fig. 2.25).

Fig. 2.24: Bone marrow biopsy

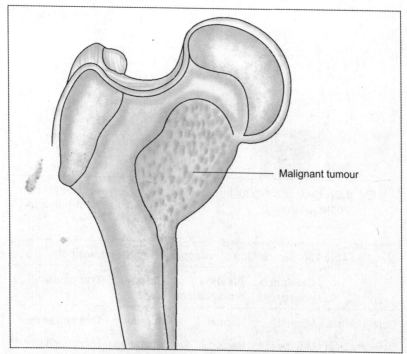

Malignant tumour

Fig. 2.25: Malignant tumour of the bone

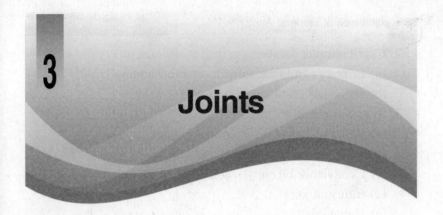

3 Joints

Related Terms

1. Arthron (G. a joint). Compare with the terms arthrology, synarthrosis, diarthrosis, arthritis, arthrodesis, etc.
2. Articulatio (L a joint); articulation (NA).
3. Junctura (L a joint).
4. Syndesmology (G. syndesmosis = ligament) is the study of ligaments and related joints.

Definition

Joint is a junction between two or more bones or cartilages. It is a device to permit movements.

However, immovable joints are primarily meant for growth, and may permit moulding during childbirth.

There are more joints in a child than in an adult because as growth proceeds some of the bones fuse together, e.g. the ilium, ischium and pubis to form the pelvic bone; the two halves of the infant frontal bone, and of the infant mandible; the five sacral vertebrae and the four coccygeal vertebrae.

CLASSIFICATION OF JOINTS

A. Structural Classification

1. **Fibrous joints**
   (a) Sutures
   (b) Syndesmosis
   (c) Gomphosis

2. **Cartilaginous joints**
   (a) Primary cartilaginous joints or synchondrosis
   (b) Secondary cartilaginous joints or symphysis
3. **Synovial joints**
   (a) Ball-and-socket or spheroidal joints
   (b) Sellar or saddle joints
   (c) Condylar or bicondylar joints
   (d) Ellipsoid joints
   (e) Hinge joints
   (f) Pivot or trochoid joints
   (g) Plane joints

B. Functional Classification (according to the degree of mobility)

1. Synarthrosis (immovable), like fibrous joints (Fig.3.1).
2. Amphiarthrosis (slightly movable), like cartilaginous joints (Fig. 3.2).
3. Diarthrosis (freely movable), like synovial joints (Fig. 3.3).

Synarthroses are fixed joints at which there is no movement. The articular surfaces are joined by tough fibrous tissue. Often the edges of the bones are dovetailed into one another as in the sutures of the skull.

Amphiarthroses are joints at which slight movement is possible. A pad of cartilage lies between the bone surfaces, and there are fibrous ligaments to hold the bones and cartilage in place. The cartilages of such joints also act as shock absorbers, e.g. the intervertebral discs between the bodies of the vertebrae, where the cartilage is strengthened by extra collagen fibres.

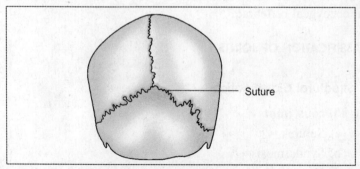

Fig. 3.1: Synarthrosis: Fibrous joint

Fig. 3.2: Amphiarthrosis: Secondary cartilaginous joint

Fig. 3.3: Diarthrosis: Simple synovial joint

Diarthroses or synovial joints are known as freely movable joints, though at some of them the movement is restricted by the shape of the articulating surfaces and by the ligaments which hold the bones together. These ligaments are of elastic connective tissue.

A synovial joint has a fluid-filled cavity between articular surfaces which are covered by articular cartilage. The fluid, known as synovial fluid, produced by the synovial membrane which lines the cavity except for the actual articular surfaces and covers any ligaments or tendons which pass through the joint. Synovial fluid acts as a lubricant.

The form of the articulating surfaces controls the type of movement which takes place at any joint.

The movements possible at synovial joints are:

Angular flexion   : decreasing the angle between two bones;

extension   : increasing the angle between two bones;
abduction   : moving the part away from the mid-line;
adduction   : bringing the part towards the mid-line.
Rotary   rotation   : turning upon an axis;
circumduction : moving the extremity of the part round in a circle so that the whole part inscribes a cone.
Gliding   one part slides on another.

C. Regional Classification

1. **Skull type:** immovable.
2. **Vertebral type:** slightly movable.
3. **Limb type:** freely movable.

D. According to number of articulating bones

1. **Simple joint:** When two bones articulate, e.g. interphalangeal joints (Fig. 3.3).
2. **Compound joint:** More than two bones articulate within one capsule, e.g. elbow joint, wrist joint (Fig. 3.4).
3. **Complex joint:** When joint cavity is divided by an intra-articular disc, e.g. temporomandibular joint (Fig. 3.5), acromioclavicular joint, sternoclavicular joint.

Fig. 3.4: Compound joint: Wrist joint

Fig. 3.5: Complex joint: Temporomandibular joint

The *structural* classification is most commonly followed, and will be considered in detail in the following paragraphs.

FIBROUS JOINTS

In fibrous joints the bones are joined by fibrous tissue. These joints are either immovable or permit a slight degree of movement. These can be grouped in the following three subtypes.

1. **Sutures:** These are peculiar to skull, and are immovable. According to the shape of bony margins, the sutures can be:
   (i) Plane, e.g. internasal suture
   (ii) Serrate, e.g. interparietal suture
   (iii) Squamous, e.g. temporo-parietal suture
   (iv) Denticulate, e.g. lambdoid suture
   (v) Schindylesis type (Fig. 3.6), e.g. between rostrum of sphenoid and upper border of vomer.
   Neonatal skull reveals fontanelles which are temporary in nature. At six specific points on the sutures in new born skull are membrane filled gaps called "fontanelles". These allow the underlying brain to increase in size. Anterior fontanelle is used to judge the hydration of the infant. All these fontanelles become bone by 18 months (Fig. 3.7).
2. **Syndesmosis:** The bones are connected by the interosseous ligament. Example: inferior tibiofibular joint (Fig. 3.8).
3. **Gomphosis** (peg and socket joint). Example: root of the tooth in its bony socket (Fig. 3.9).

nasal

temporo-parietal ~~Lambdoid~~

Saigittal

Lambdoid.

Root of tooth ~~tooth~~ *socket*

Fig. 3.6: Types of sutures

Fig. 3.7: Fontanelles

Fig. 3.8: Inferior tibiofibular joint

Fig. 3.9: Gomphosis

CARTILAGINOUS JOINTS

In this type of joints the bones are joined by cartilage. These are of the following two types:

1. **Primary cartilaginous joints** (synchondrosis, or hyaline cartilage joints): The bones are united by a plate of hyaline cartilage so that the joint is immovable and strong.

   These joints are temporary in nature because after a certain age the cartilaginous plate is replaced by bone (synostosis).

   Examples:

   (a) Joint between epiphysis and diaphysis of a growing long bone (Fig. 3.10)

Fig. 3.10: Primary cartilaginous joint

  (b) Spheno-occipital joint

  (c) First chondrosternal joint

  (d) Costochondral joints.

2. **Secondary cartilaginous joints** (symphyses or fibrocartilaginous joints): The articular surfaces are covered by a thin layer of hyaline cartilage, and united by .a disc of fibrocartilage.

   These joints are permanent and persist throughout life. In this respect symphysis menti is a misnomer as it is a synostosis. Typically the secondary cartilaginous joints occur in the median plane of the body, and permit limited movements due to compressible pad of fibro-cartilage such as in the pubic symphysis and manubriosternal joints.

   The thickness of fibrocartilage is directly related to the range of movement. Secondary cartilaginous joints may represent an intermediate stage in the evolution of synovial joints.

   Examples:

   (a) Symphysis pubis

   (b) Manubriosternal joint

   (c) Intervertebral joints between the vertebral bodies (Fig. 3.2).

SYNOVIAL JOINTS

Synovial joints are most evolved, and, therefore, most mobile type of joints.

Classification of Synovial Joints and their Movements

Type of Joint	Movement
A. Plane or gliding type	Gliding movement
B. Uniaxial joints	
1. Hinge joint	Flexion and extension
2. Pivot joint	Rotation only
C. Biaxial joints	
1. Condylar joint	Flexion and extension, and limited rotation
2. Ellipsoid joint	Flexion, extension, abduction, adduction, and circumduction
D. Multiaxial joints	
1. Saddle joint	Flexion and extension, abduction, adduction, and conjunct rotation
2. Ball-and-socket (spheroidal) joint	Flexion and extension, abduction and adduction, circumduction, and rotation

Characters

1. The articular surfaces are covered with hyaline (articular) cartilage (fibrocartilage in certain membrane bones).

   Articular cartilage is avascular, non-nervous and elastic. Lubricated with synovial fluid, the cartilage provides slippery surfaces for free movements, like 'ice on ice'.

   The surface of the cartilage shows fine undulations filled with synovial fluid.

2. Between the articular surfaces there is a *joint cavity* filled with synovial fluid. The cavity may be partially or completely subdivided by an articular disc or meniscus (Fig. 3.5).

3. The joint is surrounded by an *articular capsule* which is made up of a fibrous capsule lined by synovial membrane.

   Because of its rich nerve supply, the *fibrous capsule* is sensitive to stretches imposed by movements. This sets up appropriate reflexes to protect the joint from any sprain. This is called the 'watch-dog' action of the capsule.

   The fibrous capsule is often reinforced by :

   (a) *Capsular* or *true ligaments* representing thickenings of the fibrous capsule

   (b) The *accessory ligaments* (distinct from fibrous capsule) which may be intra or extracapsular.

   The *synovial membrane* lines whole of the interior of the joint, except for the articular surfaces covered by hyaline cartilage.

   The membrane secretes a slimy viscous fluid called the synovia or *synovial fluid* which lubricates the joint and nourishes the articular cartilage. The viscosity of fluid is due to hyaluronic acid secreted by cells of the synovial membrane.

4. Varying degrees of movements are always permitted by the synovial joints.

Classification of Synovial Joints

1. Plane Synovial Joints

Articular surfaces are more or less flat (plane). They permit gliding movements (translations) in various directions.

Examples:

(a) Intercarpal joints (Fig. 3.4)

(b) Intertarsal joints

(c) Joints between articular processes of vertebrae

(d) Cricothyroid joint

(e) Cricoarytenoid joint

(f) Superior tibiofibular

(g) Interchondral joint (5–9 ribs)

(h) Costovertebral

(i) Costotransverse

(j) Acromioclavicular with intra-articular disc

(k) Carpometacarpal (except first)

(l) Tarsometatarsal

(m) Intermetacarpal

(n) Intermetatarsal

(o) Chondrosternal (except first)

(p) Sacroiliac

2. Hinge Joints (Ginglymi)

Articular surfaces are pulley-shaped. There are strong collateral ligaments. Movements are permitted in one plane around a transverse axis.

Examples:

(a) Elbow joint (Fig. 3.11)

(b) Ankle joint

(c) Interphalangeal joints.

3. Pivot (Trochoid) Joints

Articular surfaces comprise a central bony pivot (peg) surrounded by an osteoligamentous ring. Movements are permitted in one plane around a vertical axis.

Examples:

(a) Superior and inferior radio-ulnar joints (Fig. 3.12)

(b) Median atlanto-axial joint (Fig. 3.13).

Fig. 3.11: Elbow joint

Fig. 3.12: Radioulnar joints

Fig. 3.13: Median atlantoaxial joint

4. Condylar (Bicondylar) Joints

Articular surfaces include two distinct condyles (convex male surfaces) fitting into reciprocally concave female surfaces (which are also, sometimes, known as condyles, such as in tibia). These joints permit movements mainly in one plane around a transverse axis, but partly in another plane (rotation) around a vertical axis.

Examples:

(a) Knee joint (Fig. 3.14)

(b) Right and left jaw joints or temporomandibular joint (Fig. 3.15).

Fig. 3.14: Knee joint

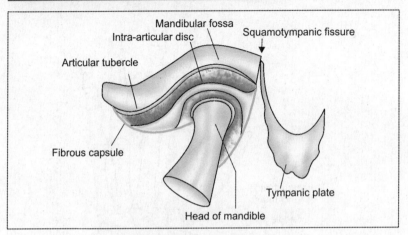

Fig. 3.15: Temporomandibular joint

5. Ellipsoid Joints

Articular surfaces include an oval, convex, male surface fitting into an elliptical, concave female surface. Free movements are permitted around both the axes, flexion and extension around the transverse axis, and abduction and adduction around the anteroposterior axis. Combination of movements produces circumduction. Typical rotation around a third (vertical) axis does not occur.

Examples:

(a) Wrist joint (Fig. 3.4)

(b) Metacarpophalangeal joints

(c) Atlanto-occipital joints.

6. Saddle (Sellar) Joints

Articular surfaces are reciprocally concavoconvex. Movements are similar to those permitted by an ellipsoid joint, with addition of some rotation (conjunct rotation) around a third axis which, however, cannot occur independently.

Examples:

(a) First carpometacarpal joint (Fig. 3.16)

(b) Sternoclavicular joint (Fig. 3.17)

(c) Calcaneocuboid joint (Fig. 3.18)

(d) Incudomalleolar joint

(e) Between femur and patella.

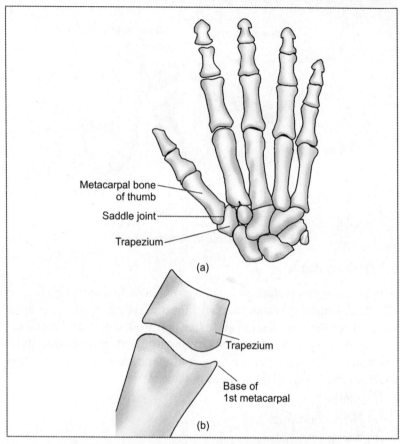

Fig. 3.16: First carpometacarpal joint: Saddle variety

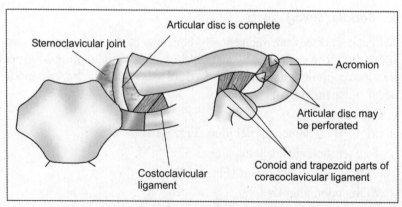

Fig. 3.17: Sternoclavicular joint: Saddle variety

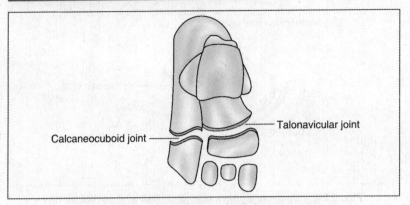

Fig. 3.18: Calcaneocuboid joint: Saddle variety

7. Ball-and-Socket (Spheroidal) Joints

Articular surfaces include a globular head (male surface) fitting into a cup-shaped socket (female surface). Movements occur around an indefinite number of axes which have one common centre. Flexion, extension, abduction, adduction, medial rotation, lateral rotation, and circumduction, all occur quite freely.

Examples:

(a) Shoulder joint

(b) Hip joint (Fig. 3.19)

(c) Talo-calcaneonavicular joint (Fig. 3.20)

(d) Incudostapedial joint

Fig. 3.19: Hip joint: Ball and socket variety

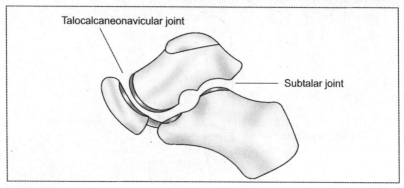

Fig. 3.20: Talocalcaneonavicular joint: Ball and socket variety

Classification and Movements of Synovial Joints

1. Terminology and Definition

Human Kinesiology: Study of geometry of surfaces and their associated movements.

Male surface: An articulating surface which is larger in surface area and always convex in all directions (Fig. 3.3).

Female surface: An articulating surface which is smaller and concave in all directions (Fig. 3.3).

Simple joints: Joints with only two articulating surfaces, i.e. male and female.

Compound joints: Joint possessing more than one pair of articulating surfaces.

Degrees of freedom: Number of axes at which the bone in a joint can move.

Uniaxial: Movement of bone at a joint is limited to one axis, i.e. with one degree of freedom, e.g. interphalangeal joints.

Biaxial: With two degrees of freedom, e.g. wrist joint.

Multi-axial: Three axes along with intermediate positions also, e.g. shoulder joint

Translation: Sliding movements of one articulating surface over the other.

2. Movements and Mechanism of Joints

Angular movement: Movement leading to diminution or increase in angle between two adjoining bones. They are of two types:

(a) **Flexion and extension:** Bending and straightening respectively.

(b) **Abduction and adduction:** Movement away and towards the median plane respectively.

Circumduction: When a long bone circumscribes a conical space. **Rotation:** Bone moves around a longitudinal axis.

(a) **Adjunct rotation:** independent rotations, e.g. locking of knee joint.

(b) **Conjunct rotation:** rotations which accompany other movements as in 1st carpometacarpal joint.

3. Shape of Articular Surface

The common articular surface shapes are:

(a) **Ovoid:** When concave–female ovoids. When convex–male ovoids.

(b) **Sellar/saddle-shaped:** These are convex in one plane, concave in the perpendicular plane.

4. Mechanical Axis of a Bone and Movement of a Bone

It is a reference point around which joint mechanics can be studied and around which the most habitual conjunct rotation occurs.

Spin: Simple rotation around the bone's stationary mechanical axis.

Swing: Any other displacement of the bone and its mechanical axis apart from spin is termed a swing.

Swing may be pure or impure (swing + element of spin).

Ovoid of motion: This represents the imaginary surface which would include all possible paths of a point on the mechanical axis at some distance from its related joint.

Cardinal swing: When the mechanical axis moves in the shortest pathway when bone moves.

Arcuate swing: When the mechanical axis moves in the longest pathway along with the bony movement.

Co-spin: When the effect of adjunct rotation is additive to the rotation.

Anti-spin: Adjunct rotation which has a nullifying effect on rotation.

Basic components of movements of the synovial joints are: (1) Spin, (2) Sliding, and (3) Rolling.

1. *Spin:* It occurs around a fixed mechanical axis.

2. *Slide*: During sliding movement, the mechanical axis of the joint and both ends of a moving bone move in the same direction. The transverse axis of movement is not fixed and it undergoes gliding or translation or linear movement.

3. *Rolling*: In rolling movement, one end of the mechanical axis moves in a particular direction and the other end moves in opposite direction. The transverse axis of movement is almost fixed. The resultant movement is rolling along

an arc. Rolling and sliding occur together in knee joint.

Joint Positions

Close packed position: When the joint surfaces become completely congruent, their area of contact is maximal and they are tightly compressed.

In this position fibrous capsule and ligaments are maximally spiralized and tense; no further movement is possible; surfaces cannot be separated by disruptive forces; articular surfaces are liable to trauma (Table 3.1).

Table 3.1: Close packed positions of the joints

Joint	Close packed position
Temporomandibular	Clenched teeth
Spine	Extension
Shoulder	Abduction and lateral rotation
Elbow	Extension
Wrist	Extension with radial deviation
Trapeziometacarpal	None
Metacarpophalangeal and	• Metacarpophalangeal flexion (finger)
	• Opposition (thumb)
Interphalangeal	• Interphalangeal extension
Hip	Extension and medial rotation
Knee	Extension with locking
Ankle	Dorsiflexion
Subtalar and mid-tarsal	Inversion
Metatarsophalangeal and	Metatarsophalangeal extension
interphalangeal	Interphalangeal extension

Loose packed: All other positions of incongruency.

Examples: Least packed position.

Shoulder – semiabduction

Hip – semiflexion

Knee – semiflexion

Ankle – plantar flexion.

Limitation of Movement

Factors

• Reflex contraction of antagonistic muscles.

• Due to stimulations of mechanoreceptors in articular tissue.

• Ligaments tension;

• Approximation of soft parts.

MECHANISM OF LUBRICATION OF A SYNOVIAL JOINT

1. **Synovial fluid,** secreted by synovial membrane, is sticky and viscous due to hyaluronic acid (a mucopolysaccharide). It serves the main function of lubrication of the joint, but also nourishes the articular cartilage.

2. **Hyaline cartilage** covering the articular surfaces possesses inherent slipperiness, like that of the ice.

3. **Intra-articular fibrocartilages,** articular discs or menisci, complete or incomplete, help in spreading the synovial fluid throughout the joint cavity, but particularly between the articular surfaces, e.g. temporomandibular joint (Fig. 3.15).

4. **Haversian fatty pads** (Haversian glands) occupy extra spaces in the joint cavity between the incongruous bony surfaces. All of them are covered with synovial membrane, and perhaps function as swabs to spread the synovial fluid.

5. **Bursa** is a synovial fluid filled bag in relation to joints and bones, to prevent friction. The inflammation of bursa is called *bursitis.*

BLOOD SUPPLY OF SYNOVIAL JOINTS

The articular and epiphysial branches given off by the neighbouring arteries form a periarticular arterial plexus. Numerous vessels from this plexus pierce the fibrous capsule and form a rich vascular plexus in the deeper parts of synovial membrane. The blood vessels of the synovial membrane terminate around the articular margins in a fringe of looped anastomoses termed the circulus vasculosus *(circulus articularis vasculosus)*. It supplies capsule, synovial membrane, and the epiphysis. The articular cartilage is avascular.

After epiphysial fusion, communications between circulus vasculosus and the end arteries of metaphysis are established, thus minimizing the chances of osteomyelitis in the metaphysis.

NERVE SUPPLY OF SYNOVIAL JOINTS

1. The *capsule* and *ligaments* possess a rich nerve supply, which makes them acutely sensitive to pain. The synovial membrane has a poor nerve supply and is relatively insensitive to pain. The articular cartilage is non-nervous and totally insensitive.

   Articular nerves contain sensory and autonomic fibres.

   Some of the sensory fibres are proprioceptive in nature; these are sensitive to position and movement, and are concerned with the reflex control of posture and locomotion. Other sensory fibres are sensitive to pain.

   Autonomic fibres are vasomotor or vasosensory.

   The joint pain is often diffuse, and may be associated with nausea, vomiting, slowing of pulse, and fall in blood pressure.

   The pain commonly causes reflex contraction of muscles which fix the joint in a position of maximum comfort. Like visceral pain, the joint pain is also referred to uninvolved joints.

2. The principles of distribution of nerves to joints were first described by Hilton (1891). *Hilton's law* states that a motor nerve to the muscle acting on joint tends to give a branch to that joint (capsule) and another branch to the skin covering the joint.

   The concept of innervation of a joint was further elucidated by Gardner (1948) who observed that each nerve innervates a specific region of the capsule, and that the part of the capsule which is rendered taut by a given muscle is innervated by the nerve supplying its antagonists. Thus the pattern of innervation is concerned with the maintenance of an efficient stability at the joint.

LYMPHATIC DRAINAGE OF SYNOVIAL JOINTS

Lymphatics form a plexus in the subintima of the synovial membrane, and drain along the blood vessels to the regional deep nodes.

STABILITY OF SYNOVIAL JOINTS

The various factors maintaining stability at a joint are described here in order of their importance.

1. **Muscles:** The tone of different groups of muscles acting on the joint is the most important and indispensable factor in maintaining the stability. Without muscles, the knee and shoulder would be unstable, and arches of the foot would collapse.

2. **Ligaments:** Are important in preventing any over-movement, and in guarding against sudden accidental stresses. However, they do not help against a continuous strain, because once stretched, they tend to remain elongated. In this respect the elastic ligaments (ligamenta flava and ligaments of the joints of auditory ossicles) are superior to the common type of white fibrous ligaments.

3. **Bones:** Help in maintaining stability only in firm type of joints, like the hip and ankle. Otherwise in most of the joints (shoulder, knee, sacroiliac, etc.) their role is negligible.

CLINICAL ANATOMY

• Intervertebral disc forms secondary cartilaginous joint between the bodies of the vertebrae. If the nucleus pulposus part of the disc gets protruded backwards, it may press on the spinal nerve leaving out from the intervertebral foramina. The condition is known as *herniation of the disc* or disc prolapse. If disc prolapse occurs in lumbar or sacral nerves, there is radiating pain in the lower limb, then the condition is called **sciatica** (Fig. 3.21).

• The joints may get dislocated, i.e. the end of one of the bones gets out of its socket. In subluxation, the end of the bone partially leaves its socket (Fig. 3.22).

• Rheumatic fever causes fleeting pain in the joints, accompanied by streptococcal pharyngitis. It is mostly temporary pain in the joints. The toxins of the bacteria may affect the mitral valve of the heart or the kidneys.

Fig. 3.21: Disc prolapse leading to sciatica

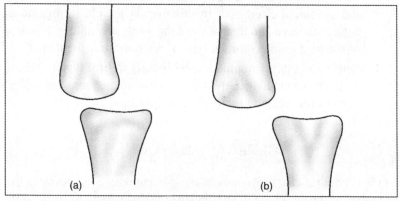

Fig. 3.22: (a) Subluxation, **(b)** Dislocation

- Rheumatoid arthritis is an inflammatory systemic disease involving the synovial membranes of small joints of the hands. Due to chronic inflammatory process there is deformity of the fingers (Fig. 3.23).
- Osteoarthritis is a degenerative condition of the large weight- bearing joints. The articular cartilage wears out, degenerates and there is formation of peripheral osteophytes. The patients feels lots of pain due to rubbing of the bones together during movements of the joints (Fig. 3.24).
- The degenerative changes or spondylitis may occur in the cervical spine, leading to narrowed intervertebral foramen, causing pressure on the spinal nerve (Fig. 3.25).

Fig. 3.23: Changes in rheumatoid arthritis with clinical features

Fig. 3.24: Osteoarthritis

Fig. 3.25: Spondylitis

Table 3.2. Comparison of Osteoarthritis and Rheumatoid arthritis

	Age and joints	Disorder and initial damage	Systemic disease
Osteoarthritis	Middle age, single large weight bearing joint	Degenerative, articular cartilage	None ESR - normal, Rheumatoid factor absent
Rheumatoid arthritis	Any age, multiple small joints of hands and feet	Inflammatory, synovial membrane	Systemic disease, ESR - raised, Anaemia + Rheumatoid factor present

• There may be injury to various structures in the joints. At times the medial meniscus of the knee joint may get injured. In that case it needs to be removed (Fig. 3.26).

Fig. 3.26: Injury to medial meniscus

• The metaphysis, the end of diaphysis or shaft is the actively growing end of the bone. In some joints, the capsule encloses the metaphysis as well. In such joints, infection from metaphysis would reach the joint cavity and cause septic arthritis (Fig. 3.27).

• There may be fracture into the joint space leading to collection of blood and broken pieces of ends of the bones in the joint cavity (Fig. 3.28).

• If joints have been diseased for a very long time with no hope of recovery, these can be replaced. The X-rays shows replaced hip joints and knee joint (Figs 3.29 and 3.30).

Fig. 3.27: Intracapsular metaphysis (black areas)

Fig. 3.28: Injury to a joint

Fig. 3.29: Right hip joint replaced   **Fig. 3.30:** Both knee joints replaced

Courtesy: Dr. Naresh Chand, Senior Consultant, Department of Orthopaedics,
Narendra Mohan Hospital, Mohan Nagar, Ghaziabad.

- Stiffness of joints related to weather. The viscosity of synovial fluid increases with fall in temperature. This accounts for stiffness of the joints in cold weather. Mobility of joint in itself is an important factor in promoting lubrication. Thus the stiffness of joints experienced in the morning gradually passes off as the movements are resumed.

- Neuropathic joint is the result of its complete denervation, so that all reflexes are eliminated and the joint is left unprotected and liable to mechanical damage. A neuropathic joint shows painless swelling, excessive mobility and bony destruction. It is commonly caused by leprosy, tabes dorsalis and syringomyelia.

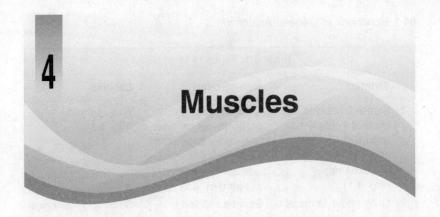

4

Muscles

Derivation of Name

Muscles (L. Mus = mouse) are so named because, many of them resemble a mouse, with their tendons representing the tail.

Definition

Muscle is a contractile tissue which brings about movements. Muscles can be regarded as motors of the body.

Types of Muscles

The muscles are of three types, skeletal, smooth and cardiac. The characters of each type are summarized in Table 4.1.

SKELETAL MUSCLES

Synonyms

1. Striped muscles
2. Striated muscles
3. Somatic muscles
4. Voluntary muscles

PARTS OF A MUSCLE

A. Two ends

1. **Origin** is one end of the muscle which remains fixed during its contraction.
2. **Insertion** is the other end which moves during its contraction. **In** the **limb** muscles, the origin is usually proximal to insertion.

Table 4.1. Types of Muscles		
Striated	**Non-striated**	**Cardiac**
1. Striated muscles are present in the limbs, body wall, tongue, pharynx and beginning of oesophagus (Fig. 4.1)	Oesophagus (distal part), urogenital tract, urinary bladder, blood vessels, iris of eye, arrector pilli muscle of hair (Fig. 4.2)	Wall of heart (Fig. 4.3)
2. Long and cylindrical	Spindle shaped	Short and cylindrical
3. Fibres unbranched	Fibres unbranched	Fibres branched
4. Multinucleated	Uninucleated	Uninucleated
5. Bounded by sarcolemma	Bounded by plasma-lemma	Bounded by plasma-lemma
6. Light and dark bands present	Light and dark bands absent	Faint light and dark bands present
7. No intercalated disc	No intercalated discs	Intercalated disc present and a characteristic feature
8. Nerve supply from cranial nervous system	Nerve supply from autonomic nervous system	Nerve supply from autonomic nervous system
9. Blood supply is abundant	Blood supply is scanty	Blood supply is abundant
10. Very rapid contraction	Slow contraction	Rapid contractions
11. They soon get fatigued	They do not get fatigued	They never get fatigued
12. Voluntary	Involuntary	Involuntary

Peripheral nuclei

Biceps brachii

Muscle fibre

Triceps brachii

Fig. 4.1: Skeletal / Striated muscle

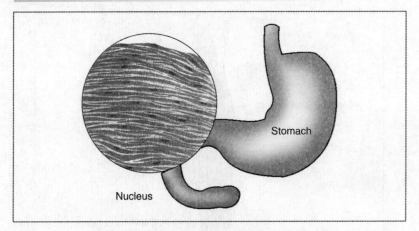

Fig. 4.2. Smooth / Non-striated muscle

Fig. 4.3: Cardiac muscle

However, the terms, origin and insertion, are at times interchangeable (e.g. climbing action of latissimus dorsi), and at other times difficult to define, as in the intercostal muscles.

B. Two parts

1. **Fleshy part** is contractile, and is called the 'belly'.
2. **Fibrous part** is noncontractile and inelastic. When cord-like or rope-like, it is called tendon (Fig. 4.4); when flattened, it is called aponeurosis.

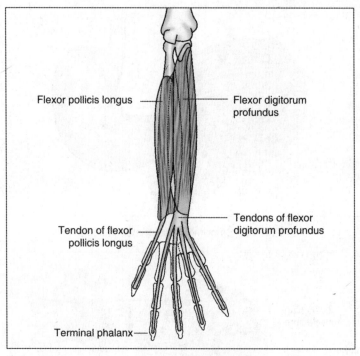

Flexor pollicis longus

Flexor digitorum profundus

Tendon of flexor pollicis longus

Tendons of flexor digitorum profundus

Terminal phalanx

Fig. 4.4: Tendons

STRUCTURE OF STRIATED MUSCLE

A. Contractile tissue

Each muscle is composed of numerous muscle fibres. Each **muscle fibre** is a multinucleated, cross-striated cylindrical cell (myocyte) 1–300 mm long. It is made up of sarcolemma (cell membrane) enclosing sarcoplasm (cytoplasm).

Embedded in the sarcoplasm there are (a) several hundred of nuclei arranged at the periphery beneath the sarcolemma and (b) a number of evenly distributed longitudinal threads called **myofibrils**. Each myofibril shows alternate dark and light bands. Dark bands are known as A bands (anistropic) and the light bands as I bands (isotropic). The bands of adjacent fibrils are aligned transversely so that the muscle fibre appears cross-striated. In the middle of dark band there is a light H band with M band (dark), in its middle. In the middle of I band there is a dark Z disc or Krause's membrane. the segment of myofibril between two Z discs is called sarcomere (Fig. 4.5).

Fig. 4.5: A sarcomere in skeletal muscle between two Z lines

B. Supporting tissue

It helps in organization of the muscle. *Endomysium* surrounds each muscle fibre separately. *Perimysium* surrounds bundles (fasciculi or myonemes) of muscle fibres of various sizes. *Epimysium* surrounds the entire muscle. The connective tissue of the muscle becomes continuous with the tendon (Fig. 4.6).

Slow and Fast Muscle Fibres (Dubowitz, 1969; Gauthier and Schaeffer, 1974)

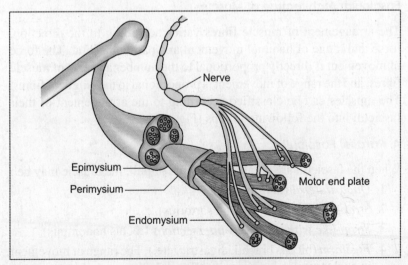

Fig. 4.6: Supporting tissue

1. **Type I (slow) fibres**

   Show a slow 'tonic' contraction characteristic of postural muscles. These are red in colour because of large amounts of myoglobin. The fibres are rich in mitochondria and oxidative enzymes, but poor in phosphorylases.

   Because of a well-developed aerobic metabolism, slow fibres are highly resistant to fatigue.

2. **Type II (fast) fibres**

   Show a fast 'phasic' contraction required for large-scale movements of body segments.

   These are paler (white) in colour because of small amounts of myoglobin. The fibres are rich in glycogen and phosphorylases, but poor in mitochondria and oxidative enzymes.

   Because of a glycolytic respiration, the fast fibres are quite easily fatigued.

3. **Intermediate fibres**

   Represent a variant of type II (fast) fibres which are relatively resistant to fatigue, although less than type I (slow) fibres (Burke et al, 1973).

   In man, most of the skeletal muscles show a mixture of fibre types, but any one type may predominate. *Force ∝ no. & size of muscle fibres*

Fascicular Architecture of Muscles

Range ∝ length.

The arrangement of muscle fibres varies according to the direction, force and range of habitual movement at a particular joint. The force of movement is directly proportional to the number and size of muscle fibres, and the range of movement is proportional to the length of fibres. The muscles can be classified according to the arrangement of their fasciculi into the following groups (Fig. 4.7).

A. Parallel Fasciculi

When the fasciculi are parallel to the line of pull, the muscle may be :

1. *Quadrilateral* (thyrohyoid),
2. *Strap-like* (sternohyoid and sartorius).
3. *Strap-like with tendinous intersections* (rectus abdominis).
4. *Fusiform* (biceps brachii, digastric, etc.). The range of movement in such muscles is maximum (Fig. 4.7).

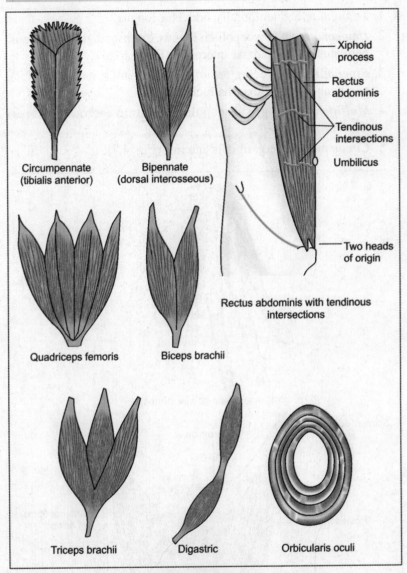

Fig. 4.7: Fascicular architecture of muscles

B. Oblique Fasciculi

When the fasciculi are oblique to the line of pull, the muscle may be triangular, or pennate (feather-like) in the construction. This arrangement makes the muscle more powerful, although the range of movement is reduced. Oblique arrangements are of the following types:

1. *Triangular,* e.g. temporalis, adductor longus.
2. *Unipennate,* e.g. flexor pollicis longus, extensor digitorum longus, peroneus tertius, palmar interossei (Fig. 4.8).
3. *Bipennate,* e.g. rectus femoris, dorsal interossei (Fig. 4.7), peroneus longus, flexor hallucis longus.
4. *Multipennate,* e.g. subscapularis, deltoid (acromial fibres) (Fig. 4.8).
5. *Circumpennate,* e.g. tibialis anterior (Fig. 4.7).

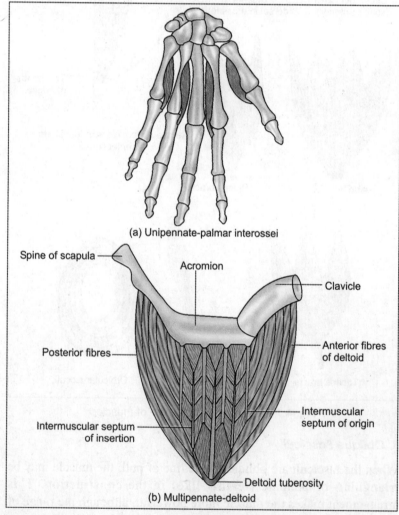

(a) Unipennate-palmar interossei

(b) Multipennate-deltoid

Fig. 4.8: Oblique fasciculi

C. Spiral or Twisted Fasciculi

Spiral or twisted fibres are found in trapezius, pectoralis major, latissimus dorsi, supinator, etc. (Fig. 4.9). In certain muscles the fasciculi are crossed. These are called *cruciate* muscles, e.g. sternocleido-mastoid, masseter, and adductor magnus.

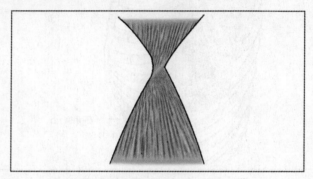

Fig. 4.9: Spiral fasciculi: Latissimus dorsi

Nomenclature of Muscles

The muscles have been named in a number of ways.

1. According to their shape, e.g. trapezius, rhomboideus, serratus anterior (Fig. 4.10), latissimus dorsi, etc.
2. According to the number of heads of origin, e.g. biceps, triceps (Fig. 4.11), quadriceps (Fig. 4.7), digastric, etc.
3. According to their gross structure, e.g. semitendinosus, semi-membranosus, etc. (Fig. 4.12).
4. According to their location, e.g. temporalis (Fig. 4.13), supra-spinatus, intercostales.
5. According to their attachments, e.g. stylohyoid, cricothyroid (Fig. 4.14), etc.
6. According to their action, e.g. adductor longus, flexor carpi ulnaris (Fig. 4.15), abductor pollicis longus, etc. orbicularis oculi (Fig. 4.7).
7. According to direction of their fibres, e.g. rectus abdominis, transversus abdominis, orbicularis oculi (Fig. 4.7).
8. A muscle with two bellies with an intervening tendon is called digastric muscle (Fig. 4.7). Muscle with number of intervening tendons or intersections is the rectus abdominis.

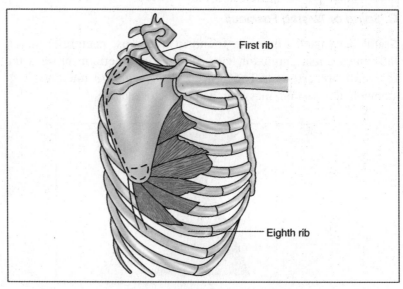

Fig. 4.10: Serratus anterior muscle

Fig. 4.11: Triceps brachii

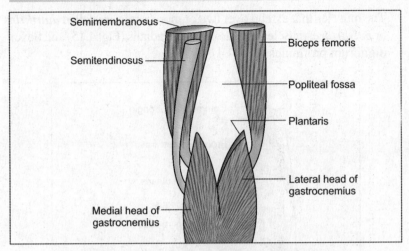

Fig. 4.12: According to gross structure: Semitendinosus

Fig. 4.13: According to shape: Temporalis

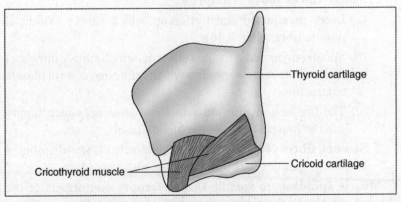

Fig. 4.14: According to attachment: Cricothyroid

The muscles that extend over two or more joints are called *diarthric* or *polyarthric* muscles, e.g. flexor carpi radialis (Fig. 4.15) and flexor digitorum profundus (Fig. 4.4).

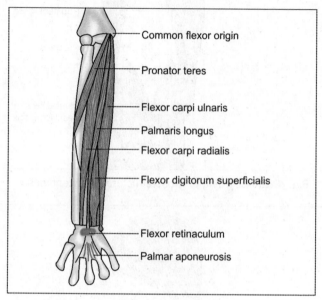

Common flexor origin

Pronator teres

Flexor carpi ulnaris

Palmaris longus

Flexor carpi radialis

Flexor digitorum superficialis

Flexor retinaculum

Palmar aponeurosis

Fig. 4.15: Muscles named according to action

NERVE SUPPLY OF SKELETAL MUSCLE

The nerve supplying a muscle is called motor nerve. In fact it is a mixed nerve and consists of the following types of fibres.

1. Motor fibres (60%) comprise:
   (a) Large myelinated alpha efferents which supply extrafusal muscle fibres (Fig. 4.16).
   (b) Smaller myelinated gamma efferents which supply intrafusal fibres of the muscle spindles which refine and control muscle contraction.
   (c) The fine non-myelinated autonomic efferents which supply smooth muscle fibres of the blood vessels.

2. Sensory fibres (40%) comprise: Myelinated fibres distributed to muscle spindles for proprioception, also to tendons.

Muscle spindles are spindle-shaped sensory end organs of the skeletal muscle. Each spindle contains 6–14 intrafusal muscle fibres which are to two types, the larger *nuclear bag fibres*, and the smaller *nuclear chain fibres* (Fig. 4.16). The spindle is innervated by both the sensory and motor nerves. The sensory endings are of two types, the primary sensory endings (annulospiral endings) around the central nuclear region of the intrafusal fibres, and the secondary sensory endings (*flower spray endings*) beyond the nuclear region on either side of these fibres.

Fig. 4.16: Nerve supply of skeletal muscle

The motor nerve supply of the spindle is derived from gamma motor neurons of the spinal cord. Muscles spindles act as stretch receptors. They record and help regulate the degree and rate of contraction of the extrafusal fibres by influencing the alpha neurons.

Motor point is the site where the motor nerve enters the muscle. It may be one or more than one. Electrical stimulation at the motor point is more effective.

Motor unit (myone) is defined as a single alpha motor neuron together with the muscle fibres supplied by it. The size of motor unit depends upon the precision of muscle control. Small motor units (5–10 muscle fibres) are found in muscles of fine movements (extra-ocular muscles). Large motor units (100–2000 muscle fibres) are found in muscles of gross movements (proximal limb muscles).

Composite/hybrid muscle: Muscle supplied by two different motor nerves with different root values is called a *composite* or *hybrid* muscle, e.g. adductor magnus, flexor digitorum profundus and pectoralis major.

Nerve Supply of Smooth Muscle

According to nerve supply the smooth muscles are classified into:

Single-unit type: Seen in intestines. The nerve impulse reaches one muscle cell, is transmitted to other cells by the mechanical pull through the fused cell membrane. The nerve supply is sparse.

Multi-unit type: Seen in the muscles of the ductus deferens. Each muscle cell receives a separate nerve fibre. The contraction is simultaneous. The nerve supply is rich (Fig. 4.17).

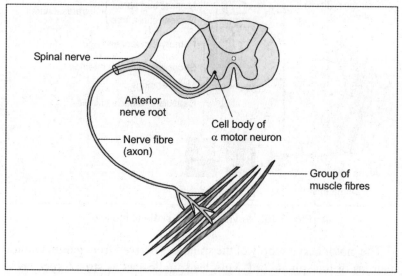

Spinal nerve

Anterior
nerve root

Nerve fibre
(axon)

Cell body of
α motor neuron

Group of
muscle fibres

Fig. 4.17: Nerve supply of smooth muscle

Nerve Supply of Cardiac Muscle

Heart is supplied by sympathetic and parasympathetic nerve fibres. Sympathetic nerves stimulate both the heart rate and blood pressure and dilate the coronary arteries. The sensory fibres convey painful impulses from heart.

Parasympathetic fibres decrease the heart rate. Their sensory fibres are involved with visceral reflexes.

ACTIONS OF MUSCLES

1. Broadly, when a muscle contracts, it shortens by one-third (30%) of its belly-length, and brings about a movement. The range of

movement depends on the length of fleshy fibres, and the power or force of movement on the number of fibres.

However, the actual behaviour of muscle contraction is more complex.

During contraction the length of the muscle may decrease (isotonic contraction).

May remain unchanged (isometric contraction).

May increase, according to the functional demands of the body.

In each circumstance the tension generated at the ends may either increase, persist, or decrease, depending upon the number and state of its active motor units and the external conditions like loading.

2. Each movement at a joint is brought about by a coordinated activity of different groups of muscles. These muscle groups are classified and named according to their function.

   (a) **Prime movers (agonists)** bring about the desired movement. When a prime mover helps opposite action by active controlled lengthening against gravity, it is known as *action of paradox*. For example, putting a glass back on the table is assisted by gravity but controlled by a gradual active lengthening of biceps (paradoxical or eccentric action).

   (b) **Antagonists (opponents)** oppose the prime movers. They help the prime movers by active controlled relaxation, so that the desired movement is smooth and precise. Thus, the antagonists cooperate rather than oppose the prime movers. This is due to reciprocal innervation of the opposite groups of muscles, regulated by the spinal cord through stretch reflex (Fig. 4.18).

   (c) **Fixators** are the groups of muscles which stabilize the proximal joints of a limb, so that the desired movement at the distal joint may occur on a fixed base. Muscles acting on shoulder joint fix it for better movement of fingers.

   (d) **Synergists:** When the prime movers cross more than one joint, the undesired actions at the proximal joints are prevented by certain muscles known as synergists. For example, during making a tight fist by long digital flexors the wrist is kept fixed in extension by the synergists (extensors of wrist). Thus, the synergists are special fixators and partial antagonists to the prime movers.

   Two or more muscles causing one movement are synergist (Fig. 4.15).

Fig. 4.18: Reciprocal innervation of prime mover and antagonist

CLINICAL ANATOMY

• **Paralysis**

Loss of motor power (power of movement) is called paralysis. This is due to inability of the muscles to contract, caused either by damage to the motor neural pathways (upper or lower motor neuron), or by the inherent disease of muscles (myopathy). Damage to the upper motor neuron causes *spastic paralysis* with exaggerated tendon jerks. Damage to the lower motor neuron causes *flaccid paralysis* with loss of tendon jerks.

• **Muscular spasm**

These are quite painful. Localized muscle spasm is commonly caused by a 'muscle pull'. In order to relieve its pain the muscle should be relaxed by appropriate treatment. Generalized muscle spasms occur in tetanus and epilepsy.

• **Disuse atrophy and hypertrophy**

The muscles which are not used for long times become thin and weak. This is called *disuse atrophy*. Conversely, adequate or excessive use of particular muscles causes their better development, or even *hypertrophy* (Fig. 1.2). Muscular 'wasting' (reduction in size) is a feature of lower motor neuron paralysis and generalized debility.

• **Regeneration of skeletal muscle**

Skeletal muscle is capable of limited regeneration. If large regions are damaged, regeneration does not occur and the missing muscle is replaced by connective tissue.

• **Hyperplasia**

Increase in number of smooth muscle fibres. Usually occurs in uterus during pregnancy.

• **Myasthenia gravis** is an autoimmune disease of muscle of unknown origin. Antibodies are produced that bind to acetylcholine receptor and block it. The nerve impulse transmission to muscle fibres is therefore blocked. This leads to extensive and progressive muscle weakness although the muscles are normal. Extraocular and eyelid muscles are affected first, followed by those of the neck and limbs. It affects more women that men and usually those between age of 20 and 40 years.

• **Polymyositis** is a disease of muscle characterized by inflammation of the muscle fibres. It starts when white blood cells (immune cells of inflammation) spontaneously invade the muscle. Muscles close to trunk or torso are mostly affected by polymyositis that results in severe weakness. Polymyositis associated with skin rash is referred to as "dermamyositis".

• **Fibrillation** is the abnormal contraction of cardiac muscle. The cardiac chambers do not contract as a whole resulting in the disruption of pumping action. In atrial fibrillation, there is rapid and uncoordinated contraction of atria, ineffective pumping and abnormal contraction of the AV node. Ventricular fibrillation is characterized by very rapid and disorganized contraction of ventricle. This leads to disruption of ventricular function.

• **Angina pectoris** is episode of chest pain due to temporary ischaemia of cardiac muscle. It is usually relieved by rest and nitrites.

• **Myocardial ischaemia**

Persistent ischaemia due to blockage of more than one arteries results in necrosis (death) of the cardiac muscle (Fig. 4.19). Pain, not relieved by rest, gets referred to left arm, chest, and neigbhouring areas.

Fig. 4.19: Myocardial ischaemia

Cardiovascular System

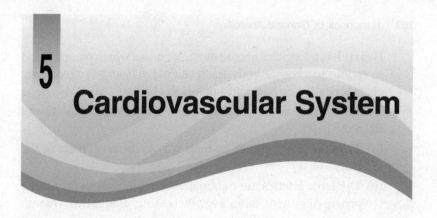

Cardiovascular system is the *transport system of* the body, through which the nutrients are conveyed to places where these are utilized, and the metabolites (waste products) are conveyed to appropriate places from where these are expelled.

The conveying medium is a liquid tissue, the blood, which flows in tubular channels called *blood vessels*. The circulation is maintained by the central pumping organ called the *heart*.

COMPONENTS

Cardiovascular system is a closed system of tubes made up of the following parts based on their structural and topographical characteristics (Fig. 5.1).

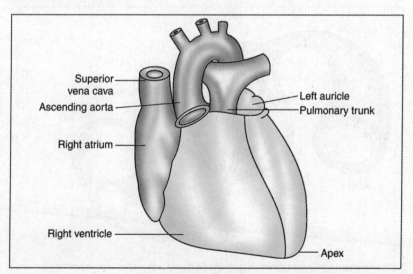

Fig. 5.1: Heart

1. **Heart:** It is a four-chambered muscular organ which pumps blood to various parts of the body. Each half of the heart has a receiving chamber called *atrium*, and a pumping chamber called *ventricle*.

2. **Arteries:** These are distributing channels which carry blood away from the heart.
   (a) They branch like trees on their way to different parts of the body.
   (b) The large arteries are rich in elastic tissue, but as branching progresses there is an ever-increasing amount of smooth muscle in their walls.
   (c) The minute branches which are just visible to naked eye are called *arterioles.*
   (d) *Angeion* is a Greek word, meaning a vessel (blood vessel or lymph vessel). Its word derivatives are angiology, angiography, haemangioma, and thromboangitis obliterans.

3. **Veins:** These are draining channels which carry blood from different parts of the body back to the heart.
   (a) Like rivers, the veins are formed by tributaries.
   (b) The small veins (venules) join together to form larger veins, which in turn unite to form great veins called *venae cavae* (Fig. 5.2).

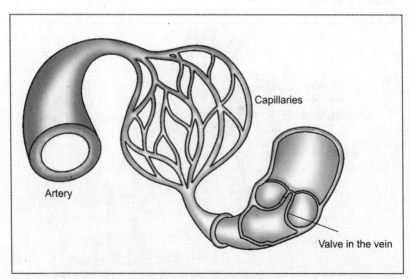

Fig. 5.2: Artery and vein

Capillaries: These are networks of microscopic vessels which connect arterioles with the venules.

• These come in intimate contact with the tissues for a free exchange of nutrients and metabolites across their walls between the blood and the tissue fluid.

• The metabolites are partly drained by the capillaries and partly by lymphatics.

• Capillaries are replaced by sinusoids in certain organs, like liver and spleen.

Functionally, the blood vessels can be classified into the following five groups.

(a) *Distributing vessels,* including arteries;

(b) *Resistance vessels,* including arterioles and precapillary sphincters;

(c) *Exchange vessels,* including capillaries, sinusoids, and postcapillary venules;

(d) *Reservoir (capacitance) vessels,* including larger venules and veins; and

(e) *Shunts,* including various types of anastomoses.

Types of Circulation of Blood

Systemic (greater) circulation: The blood flows from the left ventricle, through various parts of the body, to the right atrium, i.e. from the left to the right side of the heart (Fig. 5.3).

Pulmonary (lesser) circulation: The blood flows from the right ventricle, through the lungs, to the left atrium, i.e. from the right to the left side of the heart.

Portal circulation: It is a part of systemic circulation, which has the following characteristics.

(a) The blood passes through two sets of capillaries before draining into a systemic vein.

(b) The vein draining the first capillary network is known as *portal vein* which branches like an artery to form the second set of capillaries or sinusoids. Examples: hepatic portal circulation hypothalamo hypophyseal portal circulation and renal portal circulation (Fig. 5.3).

Fig. 5.3. Types of circulation

ARTERIES

Characteristic Features

1. Arteries are *thick-walled,* being uniformly thicker than the accompanying veins, except for the arteries within the cranium and vertebral canal where these are thin.
2. Their *lumen is smaller* than that of the accompanying veins.
3. Arteries have no valves.
4. An artery is usually accompanied by vein(s) and nerve(s), and the three of them together form the *neurovascular bundle* which is surrounded and supported by a fibroareolar sheath.

Types of Arteries and Structure

1. *Large arteries of elastic type,* e.g. aorta and its main branches (brachiocephalic, common carotid, subclavian and common iliac) and the pulmonary arteries.
2. *Medium and small arteries of muscular type,* e.g. temporal, occipital, radial, popliteal, etc.
3. *Smallest arteries of muscular type* are called arterioles. They measure 50–100 micron in diameter. Arterioles divide into terminal arterioles with a diameter of 15–20 micron, and having one or two layers of smooth muscle in their walls. The side branches from *terminal arterioles* are called *metarterioles* which measure 10–15 micron at their origin and about 5 micron at their termination (Fig. 5.4).

The terminal narrow end of metarteriole is surrounded by a *precapillary sphincter* which regulates blood flow into the capillary bed.

Fig. 5.4: Capillary bed between arteriole and venule

It is important to know that the muscular arterioles are responsible for generating peripheral resistance, and thereby for regulating the diastolic blood pressure.

Microscopically, all arteries are made up of three coats.

(a) The inner coat is called *tunica intima* (Fig. 5.5).

(b) The middle coat is called *tunica media.*

(c) The outer coat is called *tunica adventitia.* It is strongest of all coats and merges with the perivascular sheath.

The relative thickness of the coats and the relative proportion of the muscular, elastic and fibrous tissues vary in different types of arteries.

Fig. 5.5: Microscopic structure of **(a)** artery, **(b)** vein, and **(c)** lymph vessel

Blood Supply of Arteries

The large arteries (of more than 1 mm diameter) are supplied with blood vessels.

The nutrient vessels, called *vasa vasorum,* form a dense capillary network in the tunica adventitia, and supply the adventitia and the outer part of tunica media.

The rest of the vessel wall (intima + inner part of media) is nourished directly by diffusion from the luminal blood.

Minute veins accompanying the arteries drain the blood from the outer part of arterial wall.

Lymphatics are also present in the adventitia.

Palpable Arteries

Some arteries can be palpated through the skin. These are: common carotid, facial, brachial, radial, abdominal aorta, femoral, posterior tibial and dorsalis pedis (Fig. 5.6).

Nerve Supply of Arteries

The nerves supplying an artery are called *nervi vascularis.*

The nerves are mostly non-myelinated sympathetic fibres which are vasoconstrictor in function. A few fibres are myelinated, and are believed to be sensory to the outer and inner coats of the arteries.

Vasodilator innervation is restricted to the following sites.

(a) The skeletal muscle vessels are dilated by *cholinergic sympathetic nerves.*

(b) The exocrine gland vessels are dilated on parasympathetic stimulation.

(c) The cutaneous vessels are dilated locally to produce the flare (redness) after an injury. The vasodilatation is produced by the afferent impulses in the cutaneous nerves which pass antidromically in their collaterals to the blood vessels *(axon reflex).*

VEINS

Characteristic Features

1. Veins are *thin-walled,* being thinner than the arteries.
2. Their *lumen* is *larger* than that of the accompanying arteries.
3. Veins have valves which maintain the unidirectional flow of blood, even against gravity.

   Since the venous pressure is low (7 mm Hg), the valves are of utmost value in the venous return. However, the valves are absent:

   (a) In the veins of less than 2 mm diameter.

   (b) In the venae cavae.

   (c) In the hepatic, renal, uterine, ovarian (not testicular), cerebral, spinal, pulmonary, and umbilical veins.
4. The muscular and elastic tissue content of the venous walls is much less than that of the arteries. This is directly related to the low venous pressure.

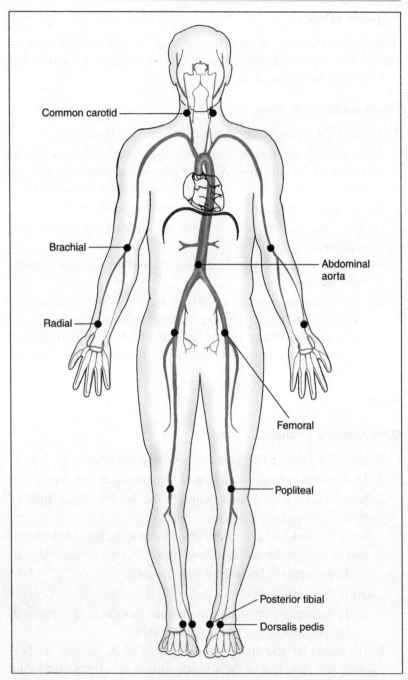

Fig. 5.6: Palpable arteries

5. Large veins have *dead space* around them for their dilatation during increased venous return. The dead space commonly contains the regional lymph nodes (Fig. 5.7).

Fig. 5.7: Dead space with large veins

Labels: Femoral artery; Femoral canal with lymph node (dead space); Femoral vein

Structure of Veins

Veins are made up of usual three coats which are found in the arteries. But the coats are ill-defined, and the muscle and elastic tissue content is poor.

In poorly developed tunica media, the amount of collagen fibres is more than the elastic and muscle fibres. The adventitia is thickest and best developed. The smooth muscle is altogether absent:

(a) in the veins of maternal part of placenta;

(b) in the cranial venous sinuses and pial veins;

(c) in the retinal veins;

(d) in the veins of cancellous bone; and

(e) in the venous spaces of the corpora cavernosa and corpus spongiosum.

Table 5.1 Shows the comparison of arteries and veins.

Table 5.1. Comparison of arteries and veins	
Arteries	**Veins**
1. Arteries carry oxygenated blood, away from the heart except pulmonary artery	Veins carry deoxygenated blood, towards the heart except pulmonary veins
2. These are mostly deeply situated in the body	These are superficial and deep in location
3. These are thick-walled, highly muscular except arteries of cranium and vertebral column	These are thin-walled
4. These posses narrow lumen	These posses wide lumen
5. Valves are absent	Valves are present which provide unidirectional flow of blood
6. These are reddish in colour	These are bluish in colour
7. These show spurty movement of blood giving pulse	These show sluggish movement of blood
8. Blood in arteries moves with pressure	Blood in veins moves under very low pressure
9. Arteries empty up at the time of death	Veins get filled up at time of death
10. If arterial wall is injured, the blood comes out like a 'fountain' in a large area all around the artery	If venous wall is injured, blood comes out, collects in a pool in a small area around vein

Blood and Nerve Supply of Veins

The larger veins, like the arteries, are supplied with nutrient vessels called *vasa vasorum*. But in the veins, the vessels may penetrate up to the intima, probably because of the low venous pressure and the low oxygen tension.

Nerves also are distributed to the veins in the same manner as to the arteries, but are fewer in number.

Factors Helping in Venous Return

1. Overflow from the capillaries, pushed from behind by the arteries (*vis-a-tergo*).

2. *Negative intrathoracic pressure* sucks the blood into the heart from all over the body.

3. *Gravity* helps venous return in the upper part of the body.

4. *Arterial pulsations* press on the venae comitantes intermittently and drive the venous blood towards the heart.

5. Venous *valves* prevent any regurgitation (back flow) of the luminal blood (Fig. 5.8).

Open venous valve

Muscle pump closed venous valve

Fig. 5.8: Venous valves and muscle pump in lower limb

6. Muscular contractions press on the veins and form a very effective mechanism of venous return. This becomes still more effective. within the tight sleeve of the deep fascia, as is seen in the lower limbs. The calf muscles (soleus) for this reason are known as the *peripheral heart*. Thus the *muscle pumps* are important factors in the venous return.

CAPILLARIES

Capillaries (capillus = hair) are networks of microscopic endothelial tubes interposed between the metarterioles and venules (Fig. 5.4). The true capillaries (without any smooth muscle cell) begin after a transition zone of 50–100 micron beyond the precapillary sphincters.

The capillaries are replaced by cavernous (dilated) spaces in the sex organs, splenic pulp and placenta.

Size

The average diameter of a capillary is 6–8 micron, just sufficient to permit the red blood cells to pass through in 'single file'. But the size varies from organ to organ. It is smallest in the brain and intestines, and is largest (20 micron) in the skin and bone marrow.

Types and Structure

The capillaries are classified as continuous and fenestrated according to the type of junctions between the endothelial cells.

1. *Continuous capillaries* are found in the skin, connective tissue, skeletal and smooth muscles, lung and brain. These allow passage across their walls of small molecules (up to 10 micron size).
2. *Fenestrated capillaries* are found in the renal glomeruli/intestinal mucosa, endocrine glands and pancreas. These allow passage across their walls of larger molecules (up to 20–100 micron size).

The capillary bed and postcapillary venules form an enormous area for the exchange of nutrients, gases, metabolites and water, between the blood and interstitial fluid. Capillaries also allow migration of leucocytes out of the vessels.

SINUSOIDS

Sinusoids, replace capillaries in certain organs, like liver, spleen, bone marrow, suprarenal glands, parathyroid glands, carotid body, etc.

Characteristics

Sinusoids are large, irregular, vascular spaces which are closely surrounded by the parenchyma of the organ. These differ from capillaries in the following respects;

1. Their lumen is *wider* (upto 30 micron) and *irregular.*
2. Their walls are *thinner* and may be incomplete. They are lined by endothelium in which the phagocytic cells *(macrophages)* are often distributed. The adventitial support is absent.
3. These may connect arteriole with venule (spleen, bone marrow), or venule with venule (liver).

ANASTOMOSES

Definition

A precapillary or postcapillary communication between the neighbouring vessels is called anastomoses. Circulation through the anastomosis is called *collateral circulation.*

Types

A. **Arterial anastomoses** is the communication between the arteries, or branches of arteries. It may be actual or potential.

1. In *actual arterial anastomosis* the arteries meet end to end. For example, palmar arches (Fig. 5.9), plantar arch, circle of Willis, intestinal arcades, labial branches of facial arteries.

2. In *potential arterial anastomoses* the communication takes place between the terminal arterioles. Such communications can dilate only gradually for collateral circulation. Therefore on sudden occlusion of a main artery, the anastomoses may fail to compensate the loss. The examples are seen in the coronary arteries (Fig. 5.10) and the cortical branches of cerebral arteries, etc.

B. **Venous anastomoses** is the communication between the veins or tributaries of veins. For example, the dorsal venous arches of the hand and foot.

C. **Arteriovenous anastomosis (shunt)** is the communication between an artery and a vein. It serves the function of phasic activity of the organ. When the organ is active these shunts are closed and the blood circulates through the capillaries.

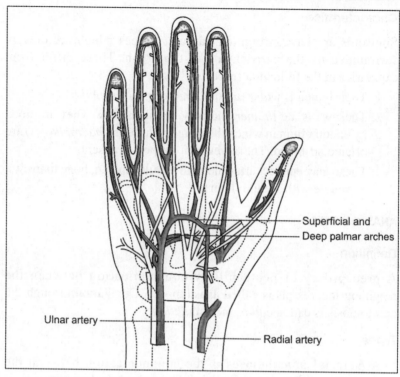

Fig. 5.9: Actual arterial anastomosis forming palmar arch

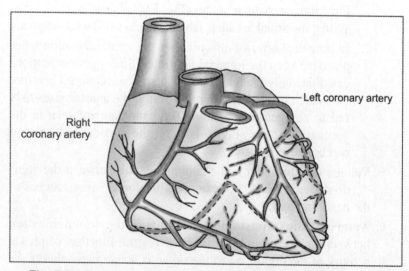

Fig. 5.10: Potential arterial anastomosis between coronary arteries

However, when the organ is at rest, the blood bypasses the capillary bed and is shunted back through the arteriovenous anastomosis. The shunt vessel may be straight or coiled, possesses a thick muscular coat, and is under the influence of sympathetic system (Fig. 5.11).

Fig. 5.11: Arteriovenous shunt bypassing the capillaries

Shunts of *simple* structure are found in the skin of nose, lips and external ear; in the mucous membrane of nose and alimentary canal; the coccygeal body; the erectile tissue of sexual organs; the tongue; the thyroid gland and sympathetic ganglia.

Specialized arteriovenous anastomoses are found in the skin of digital pads and nail beds. They form a number of small units called *glomera*.

Preferential 'thoroughfare channels' are also a kind of shunts. They course through the capillary network. Many true capillaries arise as their side branches.

One thoroughfare channel with its associated capillaries forms a *microcirculatory unit*. The size of the unit is variable from 1–2 to 20–30 true capillaries. The number of active units varies from time to time.

END-ARTERIES

Definition

Arteries which do not anastomose with their neighbours are called *end arteries* (Fig. 5.12).

Examples:

1. Central artery of retina and labyrinthine artery of internal ear are the best examples of an absolute end arteries.
2. Central branches of cerebral arteries and vasa recta of mesenteric arteries.
3. Arteries of spleen, kidney, lungs and metaphyses of long bones.

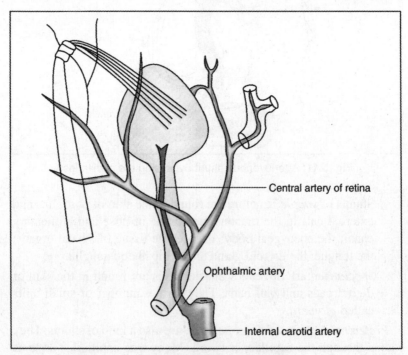

Fig. 5.12: End artery of the retina

Importance

Occlusion of an end-artery causes serious nutritional disturbances resulting in death of the tissue supplied by it. For example, occlusion of central artery of retina results in blindness.

APPLIED ANATOMY OF CVS

• The **blood pressure** is the arterial pressure exerted by the blood on the arterial walls. The maximum pressure during ventricular systole is called *systolic pressure;* the minimum pressure during ventricular diastole is called *diastolic pressure.* The systolic pressure is generated by the force of contraction of the heart; the diastolic pressure is chiefly due to arteriolar tone (peripheral resistance). The heart has to pump the blood against the diastolic pressure which is a direct load on the heart. Normally, the blood pressure is roughly 120/80 mm Hg, the systolic pressure ranging from 110–130, and the diastolic pressure from 70–80. The difference between systolic and diastolic pressure is called *'pulse pressure'*.

• **Haemorrhage** (bleeding) is the obvious result of rupture of the blood vessels. Venous haemorrhage causes oozing of blood; arterial haemorrhage causes spurting of blood (Fig. 5.13).

(a)   (b)

Fig. 5.13: (a) Spurting of blood in arterial haemorrhage, **(b)** Pooling of blood in venous haemorrhage

• **Vascular catastrophies** are of three types:
  (a) Thrombosis
  (b) Embolism

(c) Haemorrhage. All of them result in a loss of blood supply to the area of distribution of the vessel involved, unless it is compensated by collateral circulation.

• **Arteriosclerosis:** In old age the arteries become stiff. This phenomenon it called arteriosclerosis. This causes a variable reduction in the blood supply to the tissues and a rise in systolic pressure.

• **Arteritis and Phlebitis:** Inflammation of an artery is known as arteritis, and inflammation of a vein as phlebitis.

• **Atheroma** are patchy changes developed in the tunica intima of arteries due to accumulation of cholesterol and other lipid compounds. Arteries most commonly narrowed are those in the heart, brain, small intestine, kidneys and lower limbs. The changes are called thrombi (Fig. 5.14).

Fig. 5.14: Thrombi formation due to atheroma

• **Coronary arteries blockage:** These may be opened up by stents (Fig. 5.15). Blocked coronary artery may be replaced by a graft (Fig. 5.16).

• **Aneurysm** is the swelling or dilation of blood vessels where part of the wall of artery inflates like a balloon. The wall of the blood vessel at the site of aneurysm is weaker and thinner than the rest of the blood vessels. Due to its likelihood to burst it poses a serious risk to health (Fig. 5.17).

Fig. 5.15: Stent inside the coronary artery

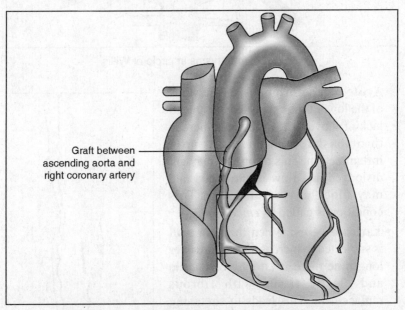

Graft between ascending aorta and right coronary artery

Fig. 5.16: Graft for bypassing the blocked coronary artery

- **Buerger's disease** (thromboangitis obliterans): This is a very painful condition. There is inflammation of small peripheral arteries of the legs. The victim is a young person and a heavy smoker.
- **Raynaud's phenomenon:** In this condition there is spasmodic attack of pallor of the fingers due to constriction of small arteries and arterioles in response to cold.

Fig. 5.17: Aneurysms in circle of Willis

- **Acute phlebothrombosis:** The veins of the lower limbs are affected. Due to lack of movement of the legs there is thrombus formation with mild inflammation. This thrombus may get dislodged and flow in the blood and may block any other artery. This condition is called as *embolism*.

- **Varicose veins:** When the vein wall is subjected to increased pressure over long time there is atrophy of muscle and elastic tissue with fibrous replacement. This leads to stretching of the vein with tortuosity and localized bulging. Venous congestion of the feet is relieved by putting feet on the stool, that is higher than the trunk, helping in venous return and relief in tiredness (Fig. 5.18). Varicose veins may occur at the lower end of oesophagus or in the anal canal.

Fig. 5.18: Varicose veins in lower limb

- At times parenteral nutrition can be given through the right subclavian vein (Fig. 5.19).
- Blood vessels can be examined in the retina by ophthalmoscope, especially in cases of diabetes and hypertension.

Fig. 5.19: Parenteral nutrition through right subclavian vein

6
Lymphatic System

Lymphatic system is essentially a drainage system which is accessory to the venous system (Fig. 6.1).

Most of the tissue fluid formed at the arterial end of capillaries is absorbed back into the blood by the venous ends of the capillaries and the postcapillary venules. The rest of the tissue fluid (10–20%) is absorbed by the lymphatics which begin blindly in the tissue spaces.

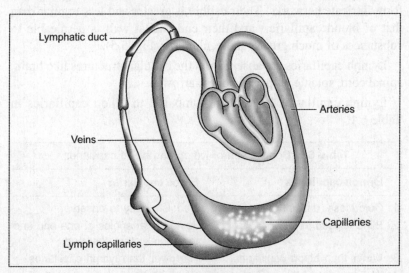

Fig. 6.1: Lymphatic system

It is important to know that the larger particles (proteins and particulate matter) can be removed from the tissue fluid only by the lymphatics. Therefore, the lymphatic system may be regarded as 'drainage system of coarse type' and the venous system as 'drainage system of fine type'.

Certain parts of the lymphatic system (lympho-reticular organs), however, are chiefly involved in phagocytosis, raising immune responses, and contributing to cell populations of the blood and lymph.

The tissue fluid flowing in the lymphatics is called lymph. It passes through filters (lymph nodes) placed in the course of lymphatics, and finally drains into the venous blood.

Lymph from most of the tissues is clear and colourless, but the lymph from small intestine is milky-white due to absorption of fat. The intestinal milky lymph is called *chyle,* and lymph vessels, the *lacteals.*

Components of Lymphatic System

The lymphatic system comprises: (1) lymph vessels; (2) central lymphoid tissues; (3) peripheral lymphoid organs; and (4) circulating lymphocytes.

1. Lymph Vessels

The lymph capillaries begin blindly in the tissue spaces (Fig. 6.2) and form intricate networks. Their calibre is greater and less regular than that of blood capillaries, and their endothelial wall is permeable to substances of much greater molecular size (Fig. 5.5).

Lymph capillaries are absent from the cellular structures like brain, spinal cord, splenic pulp, and bone marrow.

Lymph capillaries have been compared to blood capillaries in Table 6.1.

Table 6.1. Comparison of lymph and blood capillaries	
Lymph capillaries	**Blood capillaries**
1. Colourless, difficult to observe.	Reddish, easy to observe.
2. Blind (closed at the tip).	Joined to arterioles at one end and to venules at another end.
3. Wider than blood capillaries.	Narrower than lymph capillaries
4. Wall consist of thin endothelium and poorly developed basement membrane.	Wall consist of normal endothelium and basement membrane.
5. Contain colourless lymph.	Contain red blood.
6. Have relatively low pressure.	Have relatively high pressure.
7. Absorb tissue fluid from inter-cellular spaces.	Add tissue fluid to intercellular spaces.

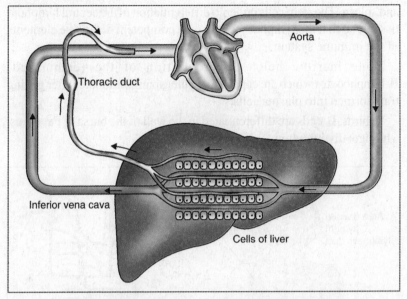

Fig. 6.2: Relation of lymphatic and circulatory system

The lymph capillaries join to form lymphatics, which are superficial and deep lymphatics. The superficial lymphatics accompany veins, while the deep lymphatics accompany arteries.

The lymph passes through filters or barriers of the regional lymph nodes which trap the particulate matter.

The filtered lymph passes through larger lymphatics and is eventually collected into two large trunks, the *thoracic duct* and *right lymphatic duct*, which pour their lymph into the brachiocephalic veins (Fig. 6.3). Thoracic duct drains both lower limbs, abdomen, left halves of thorax, head and neck and left upper limb. Right lymphatic duct drains right halves of thorax, head and neck and right upper limb.

The lymphatics anastomose freely with their neighbours of the same side as well as of the *opposite side*. Larger lymphatics are supplied with their *vasa vasorum* and are accompanied by a plexus of fine blood vessels which form red streaks seen in lymphangitis.

2. Central Lymphoid Tissues

Central lymphoid tissues comprise bone marrow and thymus.

All 'pluripotent' lymphoid stem cells are initially produced by bone marrow, except during early fetal life when these are produced by liver and spleen. The stem cells undergo differentiation in the central lymphoid tissues, so that the lymphocytes become competent defensive elements of the immune system.

Bone marrow helps differentiation of the (committed) B-lymphocytes which are capable of synthesizing antibodies after getting transformed into plasma cells.

In birds, B-cells are differentiated in the wall of the bursa of Fabricius, a hindgut diverticulum.

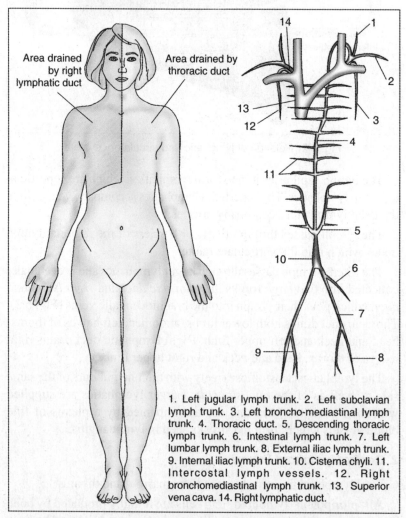

Area drained by right lymphatic duct

Area drained by throracic duct

1. Left jugular lymph trunk. 2. Left subclavian lymph trunk. 3. Left broncho-mediastinal lymph trunk. 4. Thoracic duct. 5. Descending thoracic lymph trunk. 6. Intestinal lymph trunk. 7. Left lumbar lymph trunk. 8. External iliac lymph trunk. 9. Internal iliac lymph trunk. 10. Cisterna chyli. 11. Intercostal lymph vessels. 12. Right bronchomediastinal lymph trunk. 13. Superior vena cava. 14. Right lymphatic duct.

Fig. 6.3: Area drained by thoracic duct and right lymphatic duct

Thymus helps differentiation of immunologically competent but uncommitted T-lymphocytes (10% of thymic population) which are long-lived, join the circulating pool of lymphocytes, and populate the thymus-dependent areas of lymph nodes and other peripheral lymphoid organs.

T-cells being uncommitted can react to a wide range of foreign antigenic stimuli.

These respond by cytotoxic cell killing (killing virus-infected cells, neoplastic cells, fungi, tissue grafts, etc.), by 'arming' macrophages, and by triggering the large mononuclear cells (killer cells) and the 'helper' activity of B-lymphocytes.

3. Peripheral Lymphoid Organs

Peripheral lymphoid organs comprise lymph nodes, spleen, and epithelio-lymphoid tissues (lymphoid nodules developed in the alimentary and respiratory tracts). Any part of this may become overactive on appropriate stimulation.

The progenies of B- and T-lymphocytes reach these organs where the cells may proliferate and mature into competent cells. The mature lymphocytes join the circulating pool of lymphocytes.

4. Circulating Pool of Lymphocytes

The pool contains mature progenies of B- and T-lymphocytes which may be called upon during antigenic emergencies (Roitt, 1977).

Lymphatic Follicle (Nodule)

Collections of lymphocytes occur at many places in the body. Everywhere there is a basic pattern, the *lymphatic follicle*. The follicle is a spherical collection of lymphocytes with a pale centre known as *germinal centre*, where the lymphocytes are more loosely packed.

The central cells are larger in size, stain less deeply, and divide more rapidly, than the peripheral cells.

LYMPH NODES

Lymph nodes are small nodules of lymphoid tissue found in the course of smaller lymphatics.

The lymph passes through one or more lymph nodes before reaching the larger lymph trunks.

The nodes are oval or reniform in shape, 1–25 mm long, and light brown, black (pulmonary), or creamy white (intestinal) in colour.

Usually they occur in groups (cervical, axillary, inguinal, mesenteric, mediastinal, etc.), but at times there may be a solitary lymph node.

Superficial nodes are arranged along the veins, and the deep nodes along the arteries.

Cervical lymph nodes form a ring at the junction of head and neck and vertical chains in the neck (Fig. 6.4). These drain whole of head and neck. On right side lymph vessels drain into right lymphatic duct, while on left side these drain into thoracic duct. Lymph vessels of abdominal wall above a line passing horizontally through umbilicus drain into respective sides of axillary lymph nodes. Lymph vessels below this line drain into inguinal group of lymph nodes. This line is called "watershed" (Fig. 6.5).

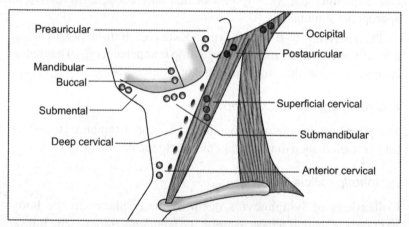

Fig. 6.4: Lymph nodes in the neck

Each lymph node has a slight depression on one side, called hilum. The artery enters the node, and the vein with efferent lymphatic comes out of it, at the hilum.

The afferent lymphatics enter the node at different parts of its periphery.

Structurally, a lymph node is made up of the following parts (Fig. 6.6).

1. **Fibrous and reticular framework:** The lymph node is covered by a capsule. From the deep surface of the capsule a number of

trabeculae extend radially into the interior of the node, where they are continuous with the fine reticulum which forms the supporting framework for the lymphoid tissue.

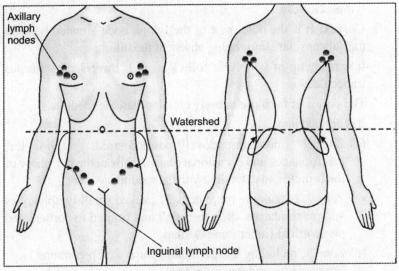

Axillary lymph nodes

Watershed

Inguinal lymph node

Fig. 6.5: Lymph vessels of anterior and posterior abdominal wall

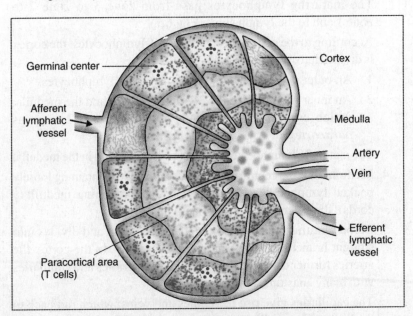

Germinal center

Afferent lymphatic vessel

Paracortical area (T cells)

Cortex

Medulla

Artery

Vein

Efferent lymphatic vessel

Fig. 6.6. Structure of lymph node (diagrammatic)

2. **Lymphatic channels:** The *subcapsular sinus* lies beneath the capsule and surrounds the node except at the hilum. Many afferent lymphatics of the node open into the subcapsular sinus. Lymph filters through reticulin fibres and leaves the node by one efferent lymphatic vessel.

3. **Cortex:** It is the outer part of the lymph node situated beneath the subcapsular sinus, being absent at the hilum.

   It is made up of lymphatic follicles and is traversed by fibrous trabeculae.

   The cortex is far more densely cellular than the medulla.

   It is divided into:

   (a) *Zone 1* containing loosely packed small lymphocytes, macrophages and occasional plasma cells in the periphery of the follicle and extending into the medullary cords.

   (b) *Zone 2*, containing more densely packed small lymphocytes and macrophages, deep to zone I and limited to cortical and paracortical (inner cortex) areas.

   (c) *Zone 3*, including the germinal centre which contains large lymphocytes and macrophages.

   The maturing lymphocytes pass from zone 3 to zone 2 to zone 1 and to the lymph sinus (Fig. 6.7).

   According to the distribution of B- and T-lymphocytes, the cortex is divided into:

   1. An outer part which contains immature B-lymphocytes.

   2. An inner part, between the germinal centre and the medulla, which contains T-lymphocytes. This part is known as *paracortex* or *thymus dependent zone*.

   The mature B-lymphocytes (plasma cells) are found in the medulla.

4. **Medulla:** It is the central part of the lymph node, containing loosely packed lymphocytes (forming irregular branching medullary cords), the plasma cells, and macrophages.

5. **Blood channels:** The artery enters at the hilum and divides into straight branches which run in the trabeculae. In the cortex the arteries further divide to form arcades of arterioles and capillaries with many anastomosing loops.

   The capillaries give rise to venules and veins, which run back to the hilum. The capillaries are more profuse around the follicles, and the postcapillary venules are more abundant in the paracortical zones for lymphatic migration.

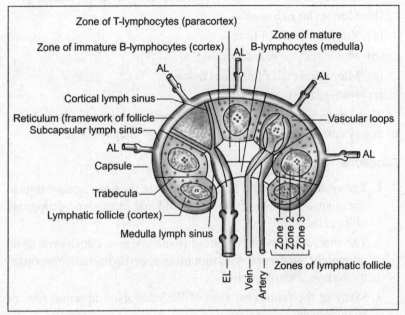

Fig. 6.7. Zones in lymph node. AL = afferent lymphatics;
EL = efferent lymphatic

Haemal Nodes

These are small lymphatic bodies resembling lymph nodes in their structure, which are found in the course of blood vessels.

The afferent and efferent lymphatics are absent. Their sinuses are filled with blood rather than lymph.

These are found in some animals in relation to their abdominal and thoracic viscera.

Haemal nodes may represent an intermediate stage between a lymph node and the spleen. In man, the spleen is a large haemal node.

Mononuclear Phagocyte System or Macrophage System (Reticulo-endothelial System)

This system is closely related to lymphatic system because the two are independent structurally and functionally. The macrophage system is made up of highly phagocytic cells which are widely distributed in the body. These cells include:

(a) Macrophages of connective tissue, reticular tissue and lungs

(b) Monocytes of blood

(c) Kupffer's cells of liver

(d) Meningocytes of meninges

(e) Microglial cells of nervous tissue

(f) Foreign body giant cells.

The endothelial cells, fibroblasts, and most leucocytes are not included in this system because of their poor power of phagocytosis.

Functions

1. The system forms first line of defence of the body against micro-organisms, because of the amoeboid and phagocytic properties of its cells.

2. The macrophages of lymphoid tissue are now considered to be intimately concerned with mounting specific immune responses by the neighbouring cells.

3. Many of the prominent sites of RES are also important sites of haemopoiesis.

Growth Pattern of Lymphoid Tissue

Lymphoid tissue of the body is prominent at birth, and grows rapidly during childhood.

The growth ceases at about the time of puberty, and is followed by partial atrophy in the later years.

This growth pattern is shared by lymph nodes, thymus, tonsils, lymphoid tissue of the intestines, and the follicles of spleen.

However, the lymph nodes may enlarge again in response to inflammation (lymphadenitis) or tumour formation (Hodgkin's disease, lymphosarcoma, etc.).

Lymph nodes are commonly enlarged by metastasis (spread) of the malignant growths (carcinoma).

Functions of Lymphoid System

1. Lymph capillaries absorb and remove the large protein molecules and other particulate matter from the tissue spaces. Thus the

cellular debris and foreign particles (dust particles inhaled into the lungs, bacteria and other microorganisms) are conveyed to the regional lymph nodes. Lymphatics (lacteals) help in transportation of fat from the gut.

2. Lymph nodes serve a number of functions.

(a) They act as filters for the lymph which percolates slowly through the intricate network of its spaces. Thus the foreign particles are prevented from entering the bloodstream.

(b) The foreign particles are engulfed by the macrophages in the sinuses.

(c) Antigens are also trapped by the phagocytes.

(d) The mature B-lymphocytes (plasma cells capable of producing antibodies) and mature T-lymphocytes are produced in the node.

(e) Both the cellular and humoral immune responses are mounted against the antigen-laden phagocytes.

(t) The circulating lymphocytes can pass back into the lymphatic channels within the node.

(g) Humoral antibodies are freely produced by the lymph nodes.

3. Production (proliferation) and maturation of B- and T-lymphocytes is the main function of lymphoid tissue.

CLINICAL ANATOMY

• Lymphatics are primarily meant for coarse drainage, including cell debris and microorganisms, from the tissue spaces to the regional lymph nodes, where the foreign and noxious material is filtered off by the phagocytic activity of the macrophage cells for its final disposal by the appropriate immune responses within the node. Thus the lymphatic system forms the *first line of defence of the body*.

While draining from an infected area, the lymphatics and lymph nodes carrying infected debris may become inflamed, resulting in *lymphangitis* (Fig. 6.8) and *lymphadenitis.* In acute cases the lymphatics are marked on the skin as painful red lines leading to the painful and tender swollen lymph nodes which may suppurate. Chronic infections (tuberculosis, syphilis, etc.) cause chronic lymphadenitis.

Fig. 6.8: Lymphangitis and lymphadenitis

- The filarial parasite lives in the lymphatics, which may become blocked, giving rise to solid oedema (elephantiasis) in the peripheral area of drainage. *Elephantiasis* is characterized by enormous enlargement of the limb or scrotum (Fig. 6.9) due to the thickened skin. The microfilariae enter the blood stream only during night and, therefore, the blood for examination must be collected during night.

Fig. 6.9: Elephantiasis involving the scrotum

- The lymphatics provide the most convenient *route of spread of the cancer cells* (Fig. 6.10). Therefore, the lymphatic drainage of those organs which are commonly involved in cancer should be studied in greater details and with special interest for many reasons:

  (a) It is helpful in the diagnosis of the primary site of the cancer.

(b) It helps in predicting the prognosis and in classifying the stage of cancer.

(c) It helps the surgeon in doing the block dissections during operative removal of the cancer.

The spread of cancer causes enlargement of the regional lymph nodes, which become fixed and stony hard. Many a time the primary site of cancer is quite insignificant or even difficult to define, and the enormous enlargement of the draining lymph nodes due to secondary malignant deposits forms the most prominent part of the disease. A retrograde spread of cancer cells, after the blockage of lymphatics, may occur by a reversed flow of the lymph.

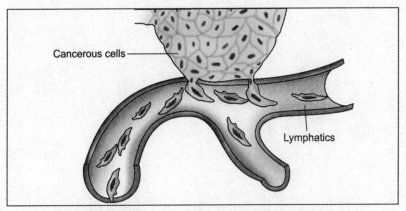

Cancerous cells

Lymphatics

Fig. 6.10: Spread of cancer cells via the lymphatics

- **Splenomegaly** is the enlargement of spleen mainly due to infections, circulatory disorders, blood diseases and malignant neoplasms. It causes excessive and premature haemolysis of red cells or phagocytosis of normal white cells and platelets leading to *anaemia*, *leukopenia* and *thrombocytopenia*. Spleen also may enlarge due to congestion of blood in portal venous congestion, in *right-sided heart failure* and in fibrosis caused due to *cirrhosis of liver*. Splenomegaly also occurs to meet the extra workload for removing damaged and abnormal blood cells. Commonest cause of splenomegaly is *malaria*.

- Enlargement of thymus may cause **myasthenia gravis**, which produces extreme weakness of the skeletal muscles. It may be treated by removal of enlarged thymus, or by drug treatment.

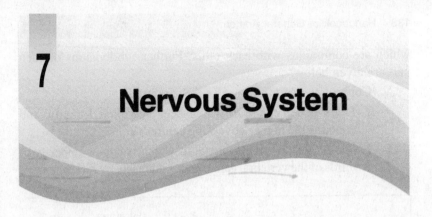

7

Nervous System

Nervous system is the chief controlling and coordinating system of the body. It controls and regulates all activities of the body, whether voluntary or involuntary, and adjusts the individual (organism) to the given surroundings.

This is based on the special properties of sensitivity, conductivity and responsiveness of the nervous system.

The protoplasmic extensions of the nerve cells form the neural pathways called nerves. The nerves resemble the electricity wires. Like the electric current flowing through the wires, the impulses (sensory and motor) are conducted through the nerves.

The sensory impulses are transmitted by the sensory (afferent) nerves from the periphery (skin, mucous membranes, muscles, tendons, joints, and special sense organs) to the central nervous system (CNS).

The motor impulses are transmitted by the motor (efferent) nerves from the central nervous system to the periphery (muscles and glands) (Fig. 7.1).

Thus the CNS is kept continuously informed about the surroundings (environment) through various sensory impulses, both general and special.

The CNS in turn brings about necessary adjustment of the body by issuing appropriate orders which are passed on as motor impulses to the muscles, vessels, viscera and glands. The adjustment of the organism to the given surroundings is the most important function of the nervous system, without which it will not be possible for the organism to survive.

Parts of Nervous System

The nervous system is broadly divided into central and peripheral parts which are continuous with each other. Further subdivisions of each part are given below.

A. **Central nervous system (CNS) includes:**

1. *Brain* or *encephalon,* which occupies cranial cavity, and contains the higher governing centres (Fig. 7.2).

2. *Spinal cord* or *spinal medulla,* which occupies upper two-thirds of the vertebral canal, and contains many reflex centres.

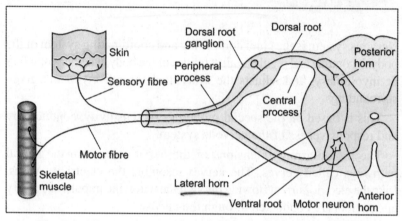

Fig. 7.1: Afferent and efferent pathways through the spinal cord

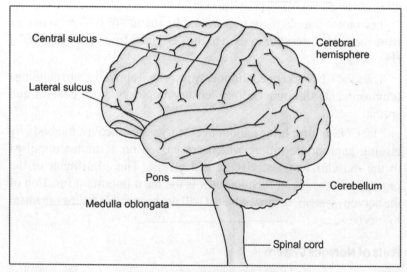

Fig. 7.2: Brain and spinal cord

B. **Peripheral nervous system (PNS)** is subdivided into the following two components.

1. *Cerebrospinal nervous system* is the somatic component of the peripheral nervous system, which includes 12 pairs of cranial nerves (Fig. 7.3) and 31 pairs of spinal nerves. It innervates the somatic structures of the head and neck, limbs and body wall, and mediates somatic sensory and motor functions.

2. *Peripheral autonomic nervous system* is the visceral component of the peripheral nervous system, which includes the visceral or splanchnic nerves that are connected to the CNS through the somatic nerves. It innervates the viscera, glands, blood vessels and nonstriated muscles, and mediates the visceral functions.

The cerebrospinal and autonomic nervous systems differ from each other in their efferent pathways. Table 7.1 shows comparison of the two systems.

Table 7.1. Comparison of cerebrospinal and peripheral autonomic nervous systems

Cerebrospinal nervous system	Peripheral autonomic nervous system
The somatic efferent pathway is made up of one neuron which passes directly to the effector organ (skeletal muscles) Neuron ↓ axon Skeletal muscle	The autonomic efferent pathway is made up of two neurons (preganglionic and postganglionic) with an intervening ganglion for the relay of the preganglionic fibre. The effector organ (viscera) are supplied by the postganglionic fibre

CELL TYPES OF NERVOUS SYSTEM

The nervous tissue is composed of two distinct types of cells:

(a) The excitable cells are the nerve cells or neurons; and

(b) The non-excitable cells constitute neuroglia and ependyma in the CNS, and Schwann cells in the PNS.

1. Neuron

Each nerve cell or neuron has:

(a) A cell body or *perikaryon,* having a central nucleus and Nissl granules in its cytoplasm (Fig. 7.4).

Fig. 7.3: Central Nervous System and 31 pairs of spinal nerves

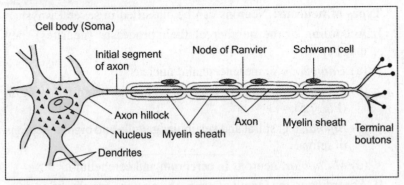

Fig. 7.4: Components of a neuron with a peripheral nerve

(b) Cell processes called neurites, which are of two types. Many short afferent processes, which are freely branching and varicose, are called *dendrites*.

A single long efferent process called axon, which may give off occasional branches (collaterals) and is of uniform diameter.

The terminal branches of the axon are called axon terminals or telodendria.

The cell bodies (somata) of the neurons form grey matter and nuclei in the CNS, and ganglia in the PNS. The cell processes (axons) form tracts in the CNS, and nerves in the PNS.

Table 7.2 shows the differences between axon and dendrite.

Table 7.2. Comparison of axon and dendrite	
Axon	**Dendrite**
1. Only one axon is present in a neuron.	Usually multiple in a neuron.
2. Thin long process of uniform thickness and smooth surface.	These are short multiple processes. Their thickness diminishes as these divide repeatedly. The branches are studded with spiny projections.
3. The branches of axon are fewer and at right angles to the axon.	The dendrites branch profusely and are given off at acute angles.
4. Axon contains neurofibrils and no Nissl granules.	Dendrites contain both neurofibrils and Nissl granules.
5. Forms the efferent component of the impulse.	Forms the afferent component of the impulse.

Types of neurons: Neurons can be classified in several ways.

I. According to the number of their processes (neurites) they may be:

(a) *Unipolar,* e.g. mesencephalic nucleus;

(b) *Pseudo-unipolar,* e.g. sensory ganglia or spinal ganglia (Fig. 7.5);

(c) *Bipolar,* e.g. spiral and vestibular ganglia and bipolar neurons of retina.

(d) *Multipolar*, neurons in cerebrum and cerebellum.

II. According to the length of axon, the neurons are classified as

(a) *Golgi type I* neurons, with a long axon; and

(b) *Golgi type II* neurons (microneurons), with a short or no axon.

Fig. 7.5: Types of neurons: **(a)** Pseudounipolar, **(b)** bipolar, **(c)** multipolar

Dynamic polarity: The neurons show dynamic polarity in their processes. The impulse flows towards the soma in the dendrites, and away from the soma in the axon (Fig. 7.6a). However, in certain microneurons, where the axon is absent, the impulse can flow in either direction through their dendrites.

Synapse: The neurons form long chains along which the impulses are conducted in different directions. Each junction between the neurons is called a synapse (Fig. 7.6b). It is important to know that the contact between the neurons is by contiguity and not by continuity. This is neuron theory of Waldeyer (1891). The impulse is transmitted across a synapse by specific neurotransmitters, like acetylcholine, catecholamines (noradrenalin and dopamine), serotonin, histamine, glycine, GABA and certain polypeptides.

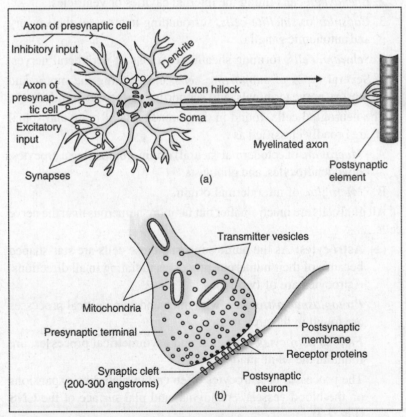

Fig. 7.6: (a) Neuron and its components, **(b)** Physiological anatomy of the synapse

The most common types of the synapse are axo-dendritic, somato-somatic, somato-dendritic. In synaptic glomeruli, groups of axons make contact with the dendrites of one or more neurons for complex interactions.

Functionally, a synapse may either be inhibitory or excitatory.

2. Neuroglia

The non-excitable supporting cells of the nervous system form a major component of the nervous tissue. These cells include the following.

1. *Neuroglial cells,* found in the parenchyma of brain and spinal cord.
2. *Ependymal cells* lining the internal cavities or ventricles.
3. *Capsular* or *satellite cells,* surrounding neurons of the sensory and autonomic ganglia.
4. *Schwann cells,* forming sheaths for axons of peripheral nerves.
5. Several types of *supporting cells,* ensheathing the motor and sensory nerve terminals, and supporting the sensory epithelia.

The neuroglial cells, found in the parenchyma of brain and spinal cord, are broadly classified as :

A. *Macroglia,* of ectodermal (neural) origin, comprising astrocytes, oligodendrocytes, and glioblasts.

B. *Microglia,* of mesodermal origin.

All glial cells are much smaller but far more numerous than the nerve cells.

(a) **Astrocytes:** As the name suggests, these cells are star-shaped because of their numerous processes radiating in all directions. Astrocytes are of two types.

Protoplasmic astrocytes, with thick and symmetrical processes are found in the grey matter.

Fibrous astrocytes, with thin and asymmetrical processes, are found in the white matter.

The processes of astrocytes often end in plate-like expansions on the blood vessels, ependyma, and pial surface of the CNS (Fig. 7.7).

The functions of various glial cells are enumerated below.

Protoplasmic astrocyte

Capillary

Fibrous astrocyte

Capillary

Microglia

Oligodendrocytes

Fig. 7.7: Types of neuroglia

(b) **Oligodendrocytes:** As the name suggests these cells have fewer cell processes. According to their distribution, the oligodendrocytes may be intrafascicular, or perineuronal.

The *intrafascicular cells* are found in the myelinated tracts.

The *perineuronal cells* are seen on the surface of the somata of neurons.

(c) **Glioblast:** These are stem cells which can differentiate into macroglial cells. They are particularly numerous beneath the ependyma.

(d) **Microglia:** These are the smallest of the glial cells which have a flattened cell body with a few short, fine processes.

They are often related to capillaries, and are said to be phagocytic in nature.

Microglial cells are possibly derived from the circulating monocytes which migrate into the CNS during the late foetal and early postnatal life.

Functions of Glial and Ependymal Cells

1. They provide mechanical support to neurons.
2. Because of their non-conducting nature, the glial cells act as

insulators between the neurons and prevent neuronal impulses from spreading in unwanted directions.

3. They can remove the foreign material and cell debris by phagocytosis.

4. They can repair the damaged areas of nervous tissue. By proliferation (gliosis) they form glial scar tissue, and fill the gaps left by degenerated neurons.

5. Glial cells can take up and store neurotransmitters released by the neighbouring synapses. These can either be metabolized or released again from the glial cells.

6. They help in neuronal functions by maintaining a suitable metabolic and ionic environment for the neurons.

7. Oligodendrocytes myelinate tracts.

8. Ependymal cells are concerned with exchanges of materials between brain and CSF.

BLOOD–BRAIN BARRIER

Certain dyes, when injected intravenously, fail to stain the parenchyma of brain and spinal cord, although they pass easily into the non-nervous tissues. However, the same dyes, when injected into the ventricles, enter the. brain substances easily. This indicates that a barrier exists at the capillary level between the blood and nerve cells. The possible structures constituting the blood–brain barrier are as follows.

(a) Capillary endothelium without fenestrations.

(b) Basement membrane of the endothelium.

(c) The end feet of astrocytes covering the capillary walls.

The barrier permits a selective passage of blood contents to the nervous tissue, and thus the toxic and harmful substances are ordinarily prevented from reaching the brain.

REFLEX ARC

A reflex arc is the basic functional unit of the nervous system which can perform an integrated neural activity. In its simplest form, i.e. mono-synaptic reflex arc, is made up of:

(a) A receptor, e.g. skin;

(b) A sensory or afferent neuron;

(c) A motor or efferent neuron; and

(d) An effector, e.g. muscle.

The complex forms of reflex arc are polysynaptic due to addition of one or more internuncial neurons (interneurons) in between the afferent and efferent neurons (Fig. 7.8).

An involuntary motor response of the body is called a reflex action. The stretch reflexes (tendon jerks) are the examples of monosynaptic reflexes (Fig. 7.9) whereas the withdrawal reflex (response to a painful stimulus) is a polysynaptic reflex.

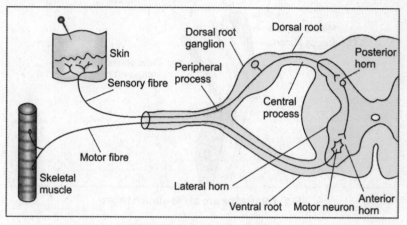

Fig. 7.8: Polysynaptic reflex

PERIPHERAL NERVES

The nerves are solid white cords composed of bundles (fasciculi) of nerve fibres.

Each nerve fibre is an axon with its coverings.

The nerve fibres are supported and bound together by connective tissue sheaths at different levels of organization of the nerve. The whole nerve trunk is ensheathed by *epineurium*, each fasciculus by *perineurium*, and each nerve fibre by a delicate *endoneurium*. The toughness of a nerve is due to its fibrous sheaths, otherwise the nerve tissue itself is very delicate and friable (Fig. 7.10).

SPINAL NERVES

There are 31 pairs of spinal nerves, including 8 cervical, 12 thoracic, 5 lumbar, 5 sacral, and 1 coccygeal.

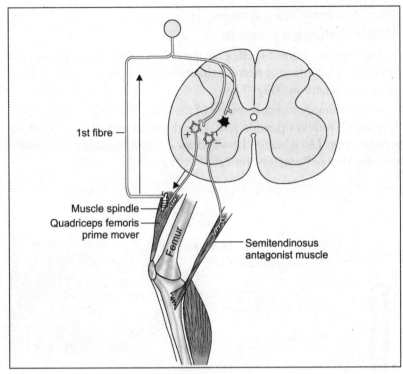

Fig. 7.9: Reflex arc of the stretch reflex

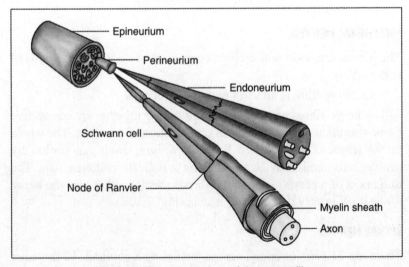

Fig. 7.10: Fibrous support of the nerve fibres

Area of skin supplied by a single segment of spinal cord is called a dermatome (Fig. 7.11). Each spinal nerve is connected with the spinal cord by two roots, a *ventral root* which is motor, and a *dorsal root* which is sensory (Fig. 7.12).

The dorsal root is characterized by the presence of a *spinal ganglion* at its distal end. In the majority of nerves the ganglion lies in the intervertebral foramen.

The ventral and dorsal nerve roots unite together within the intervertebral foramen to form the *spinal nerve.*

The nerve emerges through the intervertebral foramen, gives off recurrent meningeal branches, and then divides immediately into a *dorsal* and a *ventral ramus.*

Fig. 7.11: Dermatomes: **(a)** Anterior aspect, **(b)** Posterior aspect

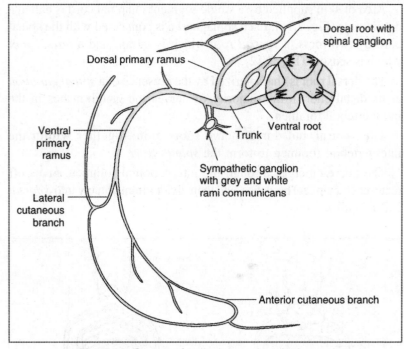

Fig. 7.12: Course of typical thoracic spinal nerve

The *dorsal ramus* passes backwards and supplies the intrinsic muscles of the back, and the skin covering them.

The *ventral ramus* is connected with the sympathetic ganglion, and is distributed to the limb or the anterolateral body wall.

In case of a typical (thoracic) spinal nerve, the ventral ramus does not mix with neighbouring rami, and gives off several muscular branches, a lateral cutaneous branch, and an anterior cutaneous branch. However, the ventral rami of other spinal nerves are plaited to form the nerve plexuses for the limbs, like the brachial plexus, lumbar plexus, etc.

Nerve Plexuses for Limbs

All nerve plexuses are formed only by the ventral rami, and *never* by the dorsal rami.

These supply the limbs.

Against each plexus the spinal cord is enlarged, e.g. 'cervical enlargement' for the brachial plexus, and 'lumbar enlargement' for the lumbosacral plexus. Plexus formation resembles a tree (Fig. 7.13).

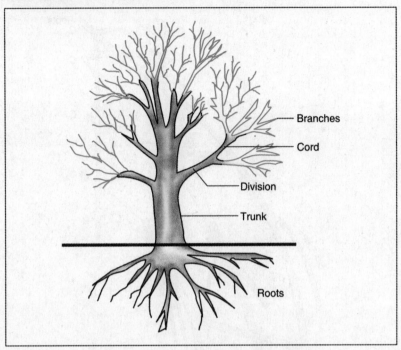

Fig. 7.13: Nerve plexus likened to a tree

Each nerve root of the plexus (ventral ramus) divides into a ventral, a dorsal division.

The ventral division supplies the flexor compartment, and the dorsal division, the extensor compartment, of the limb.

The flexor compartment has a richer nerve supply than the extensor compartment. The flexor skin is more sensitive than the extensor skin, and the flexor muscles (antigravity, bulkier muscles) are more efficient and are under a more precise control than the coarse extensor muscles.

The plexus formation (Fig. 7.14) is a physiological or functional adaptation, and is perhaps the result of the following special features in the limbs.

1. Overlapping of dermatomes
2. Overlapping of myotomes
3. Composite nature of muscles
4. Possible migration of muscles from the trunk to the limbs; and
5. Linkage of the opposite groups of muscles in the spinal cord for reciprocal innervation.

Fig. 7.14: Brachial plexus

Blood and Nerve Supply of Peripheral Nerves

The peripheral nerves are supplied by vessels, called *vasa nervorum,* which form longitudinal anastomoses on the surface of the nerves. The nerves distributed to the sheaths of the nerve trunks are called *nervi nervorum.*

NERVE FIBRES

Each nerve fibre is an axon with its coverings.

Larger axons are covered by a myelin sheath and are termed *myelinated* or *medullated fibres.*

The fatty nature of myelin is responsible for the glistening whiteness of the peripheral nerve trunks and white matter of the CNS.

Thinner axons, of less than one micron diameter, do not have the myelin sheath and are therefore termed *non-myelinated or non-medullated* (Fig. 7.15).

Fig. 7.15: Unmyelinated and myelinated axons

However, all the fibres whether myelinated or non-myelinated have a *neurolemmal* sheath, which is uniformly absent in the tracts. In peripheral nerves, both the myelin and neurolemmal sheaths are derived from Schwann cells.

Myelinated Fibres

Myelinated fibres form the bulk of the somatic nerves. Structurally, they are made up of following parts from within outwards.

1. *Axis cylinder* forms the central core of the fibre. It consists of axoplasm covered by axolemma (Fig. 7.16).

2. *Myelin sheath,* derived from Schwann cells, surrounds the axis cylinder. It is made up of alternate concentric layers of lipids and proteins formed by spiralization of the mesaxon; the lipids include cholesterol, glycolipids and phospholipids.

   Myelin sheath is interrupted at regular intervals called the *nodes of Ranvier* where the adjacent Schwann cells meet.

   Collateral branches of the axon arise at the nodes of Ranvier.

   Thicker axons possess a thicker coat of myelin and longer internodes.

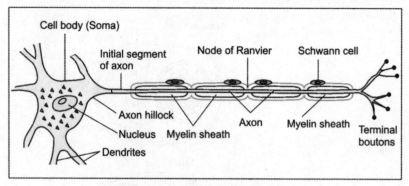

Fig. 7.16: Components of a nerve

Each *internode* is myelinated by one Schwann cell. Oblique clefts in the myelin, called *incisures of Schmidt Lantermann,* provide conduction channels for metabolites into the depth of the myelin and to the subjacent axon.

Myelin sheath acts as an insulator for the nerve fibres.

3. *Neurolemmal sheath* (sheath of Schwann) surrounds the myelin sheath.

   It represents the plasma membrane (basal lamina) of the Schwann cell.

   Beneath the membrane there lies a thin layer of cytoplasm with the nucleus of the Schwann cell.

   The sheaths of two cells interdigitate at the nodes of Ranvier. Neurolemmal sheath is necessary for regeneration of a damaged nerve.

   Tracts do not regenerate because of absence of neurolemmal sheath.

4. *Endoneurium* is a delicate connective tissue sheath which surrounds the neurolemmal sheath.

Non-Myelinated Fibres

Non-myelinated fibres comprise the smaller axons of the CNS, in addition to peripheral postganglionic autonomic fibres, several types of fine sensory fibres (C fibres of skin, muscle and viscera), olfactory nerves, etc. Structurally, a 'non-myelinated fibre' consists of a group of small axons (0.12–2 microns diameter) that have invaginated separately a single Schwann cell (in series) without any spiralling of the mesaxon

(Fig. 7.15). The endoneurium, instead of ensheathing individual axons, surrounds all the neurolemmal sheath by virtue of which the non-myelinated fibres, like the myelinated fibres, can regenerate after damage.

Classification of Peripheral Nerve Fibres

A. **According to their function,** the cranial nerves have following nuclear columns:

1. *General somatic efferent,* to supply striated muscles of somatic origin, e.g. III, IV, VI, XII.

2. *Special visceral efferent (branchial efferent)* to supply striated muscles of branchial origin, e.g. V, VII, IX, X, XI.

3. *General visceral efferent* to supply smooth muscles and glands, e.g. III, VII, IX, X.

4. *General visceral afferent,* to carry visceroceptive impulses (like pain) from the viscera, e.g. X.

5. *Special visceral afferent,* to carry the sensation of taste, e.g. VII, IX, X.

6. *General somatic afferent,* to carry exteroceptive impulses from the skin of face and proprioceptive impulses from the muscles, tendons and joints (Fig. 7.17), e.g. V.

7. *Special somatic afferent* to carry the sensations of smell vision, hearing and equilibrium, e.g. VIII.

Fig. 7.17: Functional nuclear columns of cranial nerves

B. **According to their size and speed of conduction,** the nerve fibres are divided into three categories, namely A, B and C. These have been compared in Table 7.3.

Table 7.3. Comparison of types of nerve fibres		
Group A fibre	**Group B fibre**	**Group C fibre**
1. Thickest and fastest	Medium size	Thinnest and slowest
2. Myelinated	Myelinated	Non-myelinated
3. Diameter 1.5–22 micron	Diameter 1.5–3.4 micron	Diameter 0.1–2 micron
4. Speed: 4–120 metres/sec e.g. skeletomotor fibre, (aA), fusimotor fibre afferent to skin, muscles and tendons	Speed: 3–15 metres/sec e.g. preganglionic autonomic efferents	Speed: 0.5–4 metres/sec e.g. postganglionic autonomic efferents, afferent fibre to skin, muscle and viscera
5. Fast conduction	Slow conduction	Very slow conduction

AUTONOMIC NERVOUS SYSTEM

Autonomic nervous system controls involuntary activities of the body, like sweating, salivation, peristalsis, etc. It differs fundamentally from the somatic nervous system in having:

(a) The preganglionic fibres arising from the CNS;

(b) The ganglia for relay of the preganglionic fibres; and

(c) The postganglionic fibres arising from the ganglia which supply the effectors (smooth muscles and glands).

In contrast, the somatic nerves after arising from the CNS reach their destination without any interruption (Fig. 7.1).

Autonomic nervous system is divided into two more or less complementary parts, the sympathetic and parasympathetic systems.

The sympathetic activities are widespread and diffuse, and combat the acute emergencies.

The parasympathetic activities are usually discrete and isolated, and provide a comfortable environment.

Both systems function in absolute coordination and adjust the body involuntarily to the given surroundings.

SYMPATHETIC NERVOUS SYSTEM

1. It is also known as *'thoracolumbar'* outflow because it arises from Tl to L2 segments of the spinal cord (Fig. 7.18).

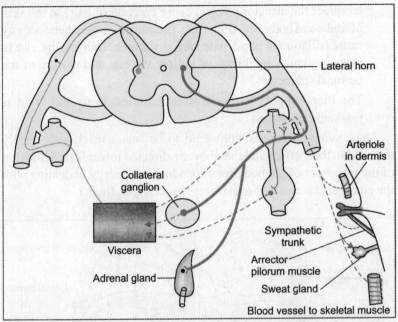

Fig. 7.18. Plan of sympathetic nervous system. Green line: afferent from viscera. Red line: preganglionic fibres. Red dotted lines: postganglionic fibres

2. The medullated preganglionic fibres *(white rami communicantes)* arise from the lateral column of the spinal cord, emerge through the ventral rami where the white rami are connected to the ganglia of the sympathetic chain (Fig. 7.19).

3. Preganglionic fibres relay either in the *lateral ganglia* (sympathetic chain) or in the *collateral ganglia,* e.g. the coeliac ganglion. The non-medullated post-ganglionic fibres *(grey rami communicantes)* run for some distance before reaching the organ of supply. The adrenal medulla is a unique exception in the body; it is supplied by the preganglionic fibres (Fig. 7.18).

4. Sympathetic nerve endings are *adrenergic* in nature, meaning thereby that noradrenalin is produced for neurotransmission. The only exception to this general rule are the cholinergic sympathetic nerves supplying the sweat glands and skeletal muscle vessels for vasodilatation.

5. *Functionally,* sympathetic nerves are vasomotor (vasoconstrictor), sudomotor (secretomotor to sweat glands), and pilomotor

(contract the arrector pili and cause erection of hair) in the skin of limbs and body wall (Fig.7.18). In addition, sympathetic activity causes dilation of pupil, pale face, dry mouth, tachycardia, rise in blood pressure, inhibition of hollow viscera, and closure of the perineal sphincters.

The blood supply to the skeletal muscles, heart and brain is markedly increased.

Thus, sympathetic reactions tend to be 'mass reactions', widely diffused in their effect and that they are directed towards mobilization of the resources of the body for expenditure of energy in dealing with the emergencies or emotional crises (fright, fight, flight).

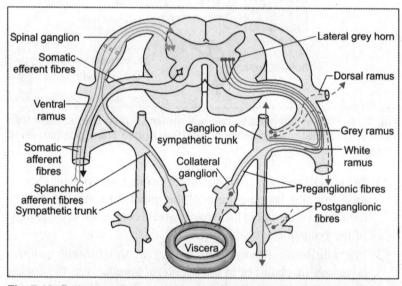

Fig. 7.19: Pathways of sympathetic and somatic nerves. Splanchnic afferent fibres (green). Sympathetic preganglionic efferent fibres (red). Sympathetic postganglionic efferent fibres (red dotted). Somatic efferent fibres (black). Somatic afferent fibres (green).

PARASYMPATHETIC NERVOUS SYSTEM

1. It is also known as *craniosacral outflow* because it arises from the brain (mixed with III, VII, IX and X cranial nerves) and sacral 2–4 segments of the spinal cord. Thus it has a cranial and a sacral part.

Fig. 7.20(a): Sympathetic nervous system

2. The *preganglionic fibres* are very long, reaching right upto the viscera of supply. The ganglia, called *terminal ganglia,* are situated mostly on the viscera and, therefore, the *postganglionic fibres* are very short.

3. Parasympathetic nerve endings are *cholinergic* in nature, similar to the somatic nerves.

Fig. 7.20(b): Parasympathetic nervous system

4. *Functionally,* parasympathetic activity is seen when the subject is fully relaxed. His pupils are constricted, lenses accommodated, face flushed, mouth moist, pulse slow, blood pressure low, bladder and gut contracting, and the perineal sphincters relaxed.

In general the effects of parasympathetic activity are usually discrete and isolated, and directed towards conservation and restoration of the resources of energy in the body.

Table 7.4 shows the comparison between the two systems.

Table 7.4. Comparison of parasympathetic and sympathetic nervous systems	
Parasympathetic nervous system	**Sympathetic nervous system**
1. All neurons forming this system originate from brain (III, VII, IX, X cranial nerves) and S2–S4 segment of spinal cord. So it is called "craniosacral outflow"	All neurons forming this system originate from T_1 to L_2 segment of spinal cord So it is called "thoracolumbar outlow"
2. Pre-ganglionic fibres are very long reaching upto terminal ganglia mostly on viscera Post-ganglionic fibres are short	Pre-ganglionic fibres are short, relay either in lateral ganglia or collateral ganglia Post-ganglionic fibres are long
3. Nerve endings are cholinergic in nature	Nerve endings are adrenergic in nature except in sweat gland
4. Functionally, it is seen when subject is fully relaxed. Parasympathetic system has no effect on skin	Functionally, sympathetic nerves are vasomotor, sudomotor and pilomotor to skin. it is seen when subject is in fear, fight and flight position. It dilates skeletal muscle blood vessels
5. Effect is discrete, isolated, directed towards conservation and restoration of the resources of energy in the body	Effect is widely diffused and directed towards mobilization of resources and expenditure of energy during emergency and emotional crisis
6. It only supplies viscera	It supplies visceral blood vessels, skin. Afferents from viscera and specific area of skin reach the same spinal segment to go to the cerebrum. Since pain is better appreciated from the skin, it appears to be coming from skin rather than the viscera. This is the basis of *referred pain* (Fig. 7.21)

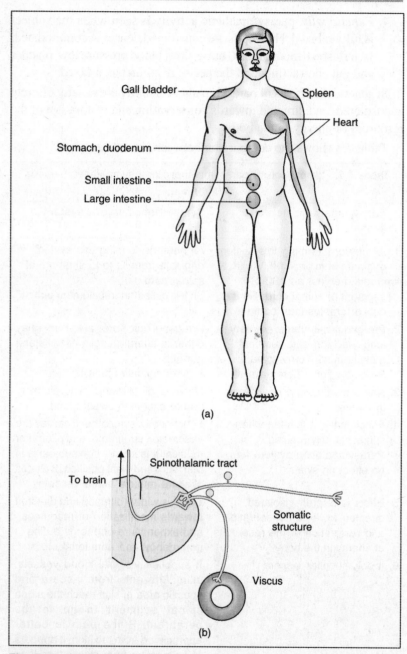

Fig. 7.21. (a) Referred pain area of skin where pain of viscera is felt; **(b)** Diagram of the way in which convergence in the dorsal horn cell may cause referred pain

CLINICAL ANATOMY

• *Irritation* of a motor nerve causes muscular spasm. Mild irritation of a sensory nerve causes tingling and numbness, but when severe it causes pain along the distribution of the nerve. Irritation of a mixed nerve causes combined effects.

• *Damage* to a motor nerve causes muscular paralysis, and damage to a sensory nerve causes localized anaesthesia and analgesia. Damage to a mixed nerve gives rise to both the sensory and motor losses.

Regeneration of a damaged nerve depends on the degree of injury, particularly on the continuity of the nerve. Different degrees of nerve injury are expressed by the following three terms.

(a) *Neurapraxia* is a minimal lesion causing transient functional block without any degeneration. Recovery is spontaneous and complete, e.g. sleeping foot.

(b) *Axonotmesis* is a lesion where, although continuity is preserved, true Wallerian degeneration occurs. Regeneration takes place in due course.

(c) *Neurotmesis* is the complete division of a nerve. For regeneration to occur the cut ends must be sutured (Fig. 7.22).

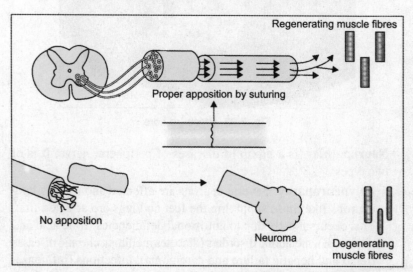

Fig. 7.22: Effects of apposition and no apposition of cut ends of nerve on muscle fibres

- Severe pain along the distribution of a nerve is called *neuralgia.* Inflammation of a nerve is marked by neuralgia with sensory and motor deficits, and is called *neuritis.*
- *Denervation* of a part produces *trophic changes.* The skin becomes dry (no sweating), smooth (loss of hair) and glazed; trophic ulcers may develop which do not heal easily. In patients with leprosy, repeated painless injuries to the tips of the fingers and toes makes them worn out and blunted.

A joint after denervation becomes a *neuropathic (Charcot's) joint,* which shows painless swelling; excessive mobility and bony destruction. The common medical diseases associated with trophic changes are leprosy, tabes dorsalis, and syringomyelia. The bed sores in paralysed patients are examples of the trophic ulcers. In general the ulcers and wounds in the denervated skin do not heal easily (Fig. 7.23).

Fig. 7.23. Pressure sore

- **Neuropathies** is a group of diseases of peripheral nerve. It is of two types:
  - **Polyneuropathy:** Several neurons are affected and usually long neurons like those supplying the feet and legs are affected first. This occurs mostly due to nutritional deficiencies (folic acid and vitamin B), metabolic disorders (diabetes mellitus), chronic diseases (renal and hepatic failure and carcinoma), infections (influenza, measles and typhoid fever) and toxic reactions (arsenic, lead, mercury and carbon tetrachloride)

– **Mononeuropathy:** Usually one neuron is affected and most common cause is ischaemia due to pressure. The resultant dysfunction depends on site and degree of injury.

• **Bell's palsy** is the compression of a facial nerve in or just outside stylomastoid foramen due to inflammation and oedema of the nerve. This causes paralysis of facial muscles and loss of facial expression on the affected side (Fig. 7.24).

Fig. 7.24. Bell's palsy on left side of face

• **Acute idiopathic inflammatory polyneuropathy (Guillain-Barré syndrome)** is a sudden, acute and progressive bilateral ascending paralysis which starts at the lower limb and then spreads to arms, trunks and cranial nerves. It is characterized by widespread inflammation with some demyelination of spinal and cranial nerves and the spinal ganglia.

• **Syringomyelia** is the dilation of the central canal of the spinal cord. Dilation of central canal develops pressure which causes progressive damage to sensory and motor neurons. Early effects are insensibility to heat and pain (dissociated anaesthesia) and in long term there is destruction of motor and sensory tracts leading to paralysis and loss of sensation and reflexes. This occurs most commonly in the cervical region and is associated with congenital abnormality of the distal end of the fourth ventricle.

- **Ageing:** Usually after 60–70 years or so there are changes in the brain. These are:
  - (a) Prominence of sulci due to cortical shrinkage.
  - (b) The gyri get narrow and sulci get broad.
  - (c) The subarachnoid space becomes wider. There is enlargement of the ventricles.
- **Dementia:** In this condition, there is slow and progressive loss of memory, intellect and personality. The consciousness of the subject is normal. Dementia usually occurs due to Alzheimer's disease.

  Alzheimer's disease: The changes of normal aging are pronounced in the parietal lobe, temporal lobe, and in the hippocampus (Fig. 7.25).

Fig. 7.25: Changes in the elderly brain

- **Infections of brain:** (a) Bacterial, (b) Viral, (c) Miscellaneous types.
  - (a) **Bacterial** (through blood) may cause meningitis or brain abscess. Otitis media may cause meningitis or temporal lobe abscess. Tuberculosis: TB meningitis is due to blood-borne infection.
  - (b) **Viral infections:** Most viruses enter through blood. Viruses may cause meningitis or encephalitis.

Herpes simplex virus and encephalitis: This virus usually causes vesicles at angles of the mouth and alae of the nose, following cold or any other disease. In some cases it may cause encephalitis.

Herpes zoster: It presents as a vesicular rash affecting one or more dermatomes. This condition is very painful (Fig. 7.26).

Poliomyelitis: The virus has attraction for anterior (motor) horn cells, especially of the spinal cord which get damaged. The nerves arising from these neurons get affected resulting in paresis or paralysis. There may be partial or complete recovery.

Vesicular rash

Fig. 7.26: Herpes zoster

(c) **Miscellaneous types,** i.e. infestations and infections.

1. **Fungal infections:** Primary infections of fungus of brain in healthy adults are rare. The fungus infections usually occur in AIDS (acquired immunodeficiency syndrome).

2. **Protozoal infections:**
   – **Malaria:** Acute malaria by *P. falciparum* may cause cerebral malaria. It is very serious condition and may cause death unless treated well in time
   – **African sleeping sickness:** The tsetse fly transmits *T. brucei* infection in man resulting in meningoencephalitis.
   – **Cysticercosis:** The larvae of tapeworm (*Taenia solium*) may form a cyst in the brain. This cyst may cause epilepsy.

3. **Parkinson's disease:** the extrapyramidal system which connects the higher centers and the anterior horn cells get affected in this disease. There is usually deficiency of neurotransmitter dopamine in the affected nuclei of the extrapyramidal system, including depigmentation of substantia nigra (Fig. 7.27).

The face is mask like and expressionless, the posture is bent forwards with stiff pill-rolling tremors of the hands.

Fig. 7.27: Gait in Parkinsonism

4. **Encephalopathy:** This condition occurs due to lack of vitamin B, especially in people who are chronic alcoholics.

5. **Upper motor neuron damage:** When the fibres are interrupted from their cortical origin till these synapse with anterior horn cells of the spinal cord. The tendon jerks are exaggerated and the plantar reflex is of the extensor type.

6. **Lower motor neuron damage:** When the anterior horn cells (motor neurons) are affected, usually by poliomyelitis virus, there is paresis or paralysis of the muscles supplied by the

nerves arising from the affected neurons. The affected muscles atrophy, and reflexes are absent.

7. **Leprosy:** There is chronic inflammation of the nerve sheaths. It is mostly associated with fibrosis and degeneration of the nerve fibres and autoamputation (Fig. 7.28).

Fig. 7.28: Leprosy

8. **Epilepsy:** Epilepsy occurs in 1% population. There is focus of hyperexcitable neurons, which get induced by various types of stimuli, causing seizures. 25% cases of epilepsy are associated with some known disease, while 75% do not show any genetic influence.

8

Skin and Fasciae

SKIN

Synonyms

1. Cutis (L); 2. Derma (G); 3. Integument. Compare with the terms cutaneous, dermatology and dermatomes.

Definition

Skin is the general covering of the entire external surface of the body, including the external auditory meatus and the outer surface of tympanic membrane.

It is continuous with the mucous membrane at the orifices of the body.

Because of a large number of its functions, the skin is regarded as an important organ of the body (Fig. 8.1).

Surface Area

In an adult the surface area of the skin is 1.5–2 (average 1.7) sq. metres. In order to assess the area involved in burns, one can follow the rule of nine: head and neck 9%; each upper limb 9%; the front of the trunk 18%; the back of the trunk (including buttocks) 18%; each lower limb 18%; and perineum 1 % (Fig. 8.2).

The surface area of an individual can be calculated by Du Bois formula. Thus, $A = W \times H \times 71.84$, where A = surface area in sq. cm, W = weight in kg, and H = height in cm.

Pigmentation of Skin

The colour of the skin is determined by at least five pigments present at different levels and places of the skin. These are:

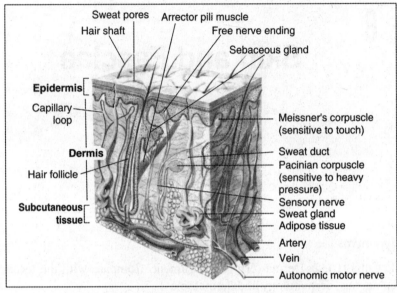

Fig. 8.1. Histological structure of skin

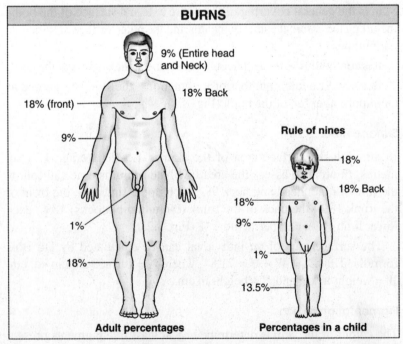

Fig. 8.2. Classification of burns

1. *Melanin,* brown in colour, present in the germinative zone of the epidermis.
2. *Melanoid,* resembles melanin, present diffusely throughout the epidermis.
3. *Carotene,* yellow to orange in colour, present in stratum corneum and the fat cells of dermis and superficial fascia.
4. *Haemoglobin* (purple).
5. *Oxyhaemoglobin* (red), present in the cutaneous vessels.

The amounts of first three pigments vary with the race, age, and part of the body. In white races, the colour of the skin depends chiefly on the vascularity of the dermis and thickness (translucency) of the keratin. The colour is red where keratin is thin (lips), and it is white where keratin is thick (palms and soles).

Thickness

The thickness of the skin varies from about 0.5 to 3 mm.

Structure of Skin

The skin is composed of two distinct layers, epidermis and dermis.

A. Epidermis

It is the superficial, avascular layer of stratified squamous epithelium. It is ectodermal in origin and gives rise to the appendages of the skin, namely hair, nails, sweat glands and sebaceous glands.

Structurally, the epidermis is made up of a superficial *cornified zone* and a deep *germinative zone.* The cells of the deepest layer proliferate and pass towards the surface to replace the cornified cells lost due to wear and tear. As the cells migrate superficially, they become more and more flattened, and lose their nuclei to form the flattened dead cells of the stratum corneum. In the germinative zone, there are also 'dopa' positive *melanocytes* (melanoblasts, dendritic cells, or clear cells) of neural crest origin, which synthesize melanin.

B. Dermis or corium

Dermis or corium is the deep, vascular layer of the skin, derived from mesoderm.

It is made up of connective tissue (with variable elastic fibres) mixed with blood vessels, lymphatics and nerves. The connective tissue is arranged into a superficial *papillary layer* and a deep *reticular layer.*

The papillary layer forms conical, blunt projections (dermal papillae) which fit into reciprocal depressions on the undersurface of the epidermis. The reticular layer is composed chiefly of the white fibrous tissue arranged mostly in parallel bundles.

The direction of the bundles, constituting flexor or *cleavage lines* (Langer's lines), is longitudinal in the limbs and horizontal in the trunk and neck (Fig. 8.3).

Fig. 8.3. Flexure lines (Langer's lines)

In old age the elastic fibres atrophy and the skin becomes wrinkled. Overstretching of the skin may lead to rupture of the fibres, followed by scar formation. These scars appear as white streaks on the skin (e.g. lineae gravidarum).

At the *flexure lines* of the joints, the skin is firmly adherent to the underlying deep fascia. Dermis is the real skin, because, when dried it makes green hide, and when tanned it makes leather. Its deep surface is continuous with the superficial fascia.

Surface Irregularities of the Skin

The skin is marked by three types of surface irregularities, the tension lines, flexure lines and papillary ridges (Montagna and Lobitz, 1964).

1. **Tension lines:** Form a network of linear furrows which divide the surface into polygonal or lozenge-shaped areas. These lines to some extent correspond to variations in the pattern of fibres in the dermis.

2. **Flexure lines (skin creases or skin joints):** Are certain permanent lines along which the skin folds during habitual movements (chiefly flexion) of the joints.

   The skin along these lines is thin and firmly bound to the deep fascia.

   The lines are prominent opposite the flexure of the joints, particularly on the palms, soles and digits (Fig. 8.4).

Fig. 8.4: Flexure lines

3. **Papillary ridges (friction ridges):** Are confined to palms and soles and their digits.

   They form narrow ridges separated by fine parallel grooves, arranged in curved arrays.

   They correspond to patterns of dermal papillae. Their study constitutes a branch of science, called dermatoglyphics (Cummins and Midlo, 1961).

   Three major patterns in the human fingerprints include loops, whorls and arches.

   These patterns and many other minor features are determined genetically by multifactorial inheritance (Fig. 8.5).

Fig. 8.5. Close up of a finger tip showing characteristic ridges that form a fingerprint pattern unique for every individual

APPENDAGES OF SKIN

1. Nails

Synonyms. (a) Onych or onycho (G); and (b) ungues (L). Compare with the terms paronychia, koilonychia and onychomycosis (Fig. 8.6).

Nails are hardened keratin plates (cornified zone) on the dorsal surface of the tips of fingers and toes, acting as a rigid support for the digital pads of terminal phalanges. Each nail has the following parts.

   (a) *Root* is the proximal hidden part which is burried into the nail groove and is overlapped by the nail fold of the skin.
   (b) *Free border* is the distal part free from the skin.
   (c) *Body* is the exposed part of the nail which is adherent to the underlying skin.

The proximal part of the body presents a white opaque crescent called *lunule.*

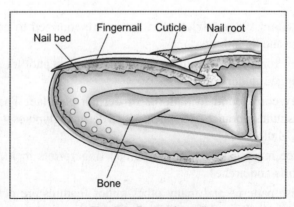

Fig. 8.6: Parts of a nail

Each lateral border of the nail body is overlapped by a fold of a skin, termed the *nail wall.*

The skin (germinative zone + corium) beneath the root and body of the nail is called *nail bed.* The germinative zone of the nail bed beneath the root and lunule is thick and proliferative (germinal matrix), and is responsible for the growth of the nail.

The rest of the nail bed is thin (sterile matrix) over which the growing nail glides.

Under the translucent body (except lunule) of the nail, the corium is very vascular. This accounts for their pink colour.

CLINICAL ANATOMY

- In anaemia the nails are pale and white.
- In iron deficiency anaemia the nails become thin, brittle and spoon-shaped (koilonychia).
- Hypertrophy of the nail bed *(clubbing)* occurs in chronic suppurative disease (lung abscess, bronchiectasis, osteomyelitis) and in severe type of cyanosis (Fallot's tetralogy, chronic congestive cardiac failure).
- Disturbances of nail growth due to acute illness or trauma give rise to transverse grooves in the nail substance, which move distally with the nail growth. Since the average rate of growth is about 0.1 mm per day or 3 mm per month, the date of the past illness can be estimated.
- It takes about 90–120 days for the whole nail (body) to grow. Therefore, in fungal diseases of the nails the course of treatment should last for not less than this period. The growth is faster in summer than in winter, in the fingers than in toes, and in the longer fingers than in the shorter ones.
- Hairs exhibit alterations in certain diseases. In malnutrition hairs become thin, dry and sparse; in hypothyroidism they become coarse and dry.
- Excessive growth of hair *(hirsutism)* occurs in adrenogenital syndrome. Loss of hair is known as *alopecia.*
- Skin is dry in 'Dhatura' poisoning, heat stroke, and diabetic coma; it is unusually moist in hypoglycaemic coma, and peripheral failure.

- In *ichthyosis* (characterized by abnormally dry skin), the sebaceous glands are few and small, and the secretion of sebum is markedly reduced. Excessive oiliness of skin, due to overactivity of sebaceous glands, is called *seborrhoea*. It may occur from puberty onwards, but diminishes with advancing age.

- *Acne vulgaris* is a common complication of seborrhoea. Seborrhoeic skin is susceptible to infections *(seborrhoeic dermatitis* or *furunculosis)* and to chemical irritants (chemical folliculitis and dermatitis).

2. Hair

Hair are keratinous filaments derived from invaginations of the germinative layer of epidermis into the dermis.

These are peculiar to mammals (like feathers to the birds), and help in conservation of their body heat.

However, in man the heat loss is prevented by the cutaneous sensation of touch.

Hair are distributed all over the body, except for the palms, soles, dorsal surface of distal phalanges, umbilicus, glans penis, inner surface of prepuce, the labia minora, and inner surface of labia majora. The length, thickness and colour of the hair vary in different part of the body and in different individuals.

Each hair has an implanted part called the *root,* and a projecting part called the *shaft.*

The root is surrounded by a *hair follicle* (a sheath of epidermis and dermis), and is expanded at its proximal end to form the *hair bulb.*

Each hair bulb is invaginated at its end by the *hair papilla* (vascular connective tissue) which forms the neurovascular hilum of the hair and its sheath.

Hair grows at the hair bulb, by proliferation of its cells capping the papilla.

The hair follicles, enclosing hair roots, lie obliquely to the surface of the skin, which is responsible for the characteristic hair streams in different parts of the body.

The *arrectores pilorum* muscles (smooth muscles supplied by sympathetic nerves) connect the undersurface of the follicles to the superficial part of the dermis.

Contraction of these muscles leads to erection of hair, squeezes out the sebum, and produces 'goose skin' (Fig. 8.1).

The foetal skin is covered by fine hair called *lanugo* (primary hair). These are mostly shed by birth, and are replaced during infancy by another set of fine hair called *vellus* (secondary hair).

These are retained in most parts of the body, but are replaced by the thick and dark *terminal hair* of the scalp and eyebrows, and other hairy areas of the adult skin.

The hair grow at the rate of about 1.5–2.2 mm per week; their growth is controlled by hormones.

The life span of the hair varies from 4 months (eyelashes, axillary hair) to 4 years (scalp hair).

3. Sweat Glands

Sudoriferous or sweat glands are distributed all over the skin, except for the lips, glans penis, and nail bed. These glands are of two types, *eccrine* and *apocrine* (Zelickson, 1971).

The **eccrine glands** are much more abundant and distributed in almost every part of the skin.

Each gland is a single tube, the deep part of which is coiled into a ball.

The coiled part, called the *body* of the gland, lies in the deeper part of corium or in the subcutaneous tissue.

The straight part, called the *duct,* traverses the dermis and epidermis and opens on the surface of the skin.

The glands are large in the axilla and groin, most numerous in the palms and soles, and least numerous in the neck and back.

The eccrine glands are *merocrine* in nature, i.e. produce their thin watery secretion without any disintegration of the epithelial cells.

They are supplied and controlled by *cholinergic sympathetic nerves.*

The glands help in regulation of the body temperature by evaporation of sweat, and also help in excreting the body salts.

In dogs, sweat glands are confined to foot pads. Therefore, dogs do not sweat, they pant.

The **apocrine glands** are confined to axilla, eyelids (Moll's glands), nipple and areola of the breast, perianal region, and the external genitalia.

They are larger than eccrine glands and produce a thicker secretion having a characteristic odour. They develop in close association with hair and their ducts typically open into the distal ends of the hair follicles.

Ceruminous glands of the external auditory meatus are modified apocrine sweat glands.

The apocrine glands also are merocrine in nature, but are regulated by a dual autonomic control. Some workers are not inclined to call them as sweat glands at all because they do not respond sufficiently to temperature changes.

In animals they produce chemical signals or pheromones, which are important in courtship and social behaviour.

On an average one litre of sweat is secreted per day; another 400 ml of water is lost through the lungs, and 100 ml through the faeces.

This makes a total of about 1500 ml, a rough estimate of the invisible loss of water per day.

However, in hot climates the secretion of sweat may amount to 3–10 litres per day, with a maximum of 1–2 litres per hour.

So long the sweat glands are intact, the skin can regenerate. If the sweat glands are lost, skin grafting becomes necessary.

4. Sebaceous Glands

Sebaceous glands, producing an oily secretion, are widely distributed all over the dermis of the skin (Fig. 8.7), except for the palms and soles. They are especially abundant in the scalp and face, and are also very numerous around the apertures of the ear, nose, mouth, and anus.

Sebaceous glands are small and sacculated in appearance, made up of a cluster of about 2–5 piriform alveoli.

Their ducts open into the hair follicles, with the exception of lips, glans penis, inner surface of prepuce, labia minora, nipple and areola of the breast, and tarsal glands of the eyelids, where the ducts open on the surface of the skin.

Sebaceous glands are *holocrine* in nature, i.e. they produce their secretion by complete fatty degeneration of the central cells of the alveolus, which are then replaced by the proliferating peripheral cells.

The secretion is under *hormonal control,* especially the androgens.

The oily secretion of sebaceous glands is called *sebum.*

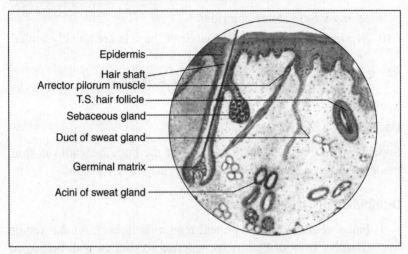

Fig. 8.7: Sebaceous gland between hair and arrector pilorum muscle

It lubricates skin and protects it from moisture, desiccation, and the harmful sun rays. Sebum also lubricates hair and prevents them from becoming brittle.

In addition, sebum also has some bactericidal action.

Sebum makes the skin water-proof. Water evaporates from the skin, but the fats and oils are absorbed by it.

Functions of Skin

1. *Protection.* Skin protects the body from mechanical injuries, bacterial infections, heat and cold, wet and drought, acid and alkali, and the actinic rays of the sun.
2. *Sensory.* Skin is sensory to touch, pain and temperature.
3. *Regulation of body temperature.* Heat is lost through evaporation of sweat; and heat is conserved by the fat and hair.
4. *Absorption.* Oily substances are freely absorbed by the skin.
5. *Secretion.* Skin secretes sweat and sebum.
6. *Excretion.* The excess of water, salts and waste products are excreted through the sweat.
7. *Regulation of pH.* A good amount of acid is excreted through the sweat.
8. *Synthesis.* In the skin, vitamin D is synthesized from ergosterol by the action of ultraviolet rays of the sun.

9. *Storage.* Skin stores chlorides.

10. *Reparative.* The cuts and wounds of the skin are quickly healed.

SUPERFICIAL FASCIA

Definition

Superficial fascia is a general coating of the body beneath the skin, made up of loose areolar tissue with varying amounts of fat.

Distribution of Fat in this Fascia

1. Fat is *abundant* in the gluteal region (buttocks), lumbar region (flanks), front of the thighs, anterior abdominal wall below the umbilicus, mammary gland (Fig. 8.8), postdeltoid region, and the cervicothoracic region.

2. In *females,* fat is more abundant and is more evenly distributed than in males.

3. Fat is *absent* from the eyelids, external ear, penis, and scrotum.

4. The subcutaneous layer of fat is called the *panniculus adiposus.*

In females fat is in the superficial fascia of the lower abdomen, upper thigh, whereas in males it is inside the abdominal cavity.

In general, in women fat forms a thicker and more even layer than in men.

Fig. 8.8: Fat in mammary gland

Fat (adipose tissue) fills the hollow spaces like axilla, orbits and ischiorectal fossa.

Fat present around the kidneys in abdomen, supports these organs.

Types of Fats

There are two types of fat, i.e. yellow and brown fat.

Most of the body fat is yellow, only in hibernating animals it is brown. The cells of brown fat are smaller with several small droplets, and multiple mitochondria.

Fat cells are specialised cells, and the size of fat cells increases during accumulation of fat, rather than the number of cells.

Any attempt to reduce excessive fat (obesity) must be slow and steady and not drastic, as the latter may cause harm to the body.

Important Features

1. Superficial fascia is *most distinct* in the lower part of the anterior abdominal wall, perineum, and the limbs.
2. It is *very thin* on the dorsal aspect of the hands and feet, sides of the neck, face, and around the anus.
3. It is *very dense* in the scalp, palms, and soles.
4. Superficial fascia shows *stratification* (into two layers) in the lower part of anterior abdominal wall, perineum, and uppermost part of the thighs.
5. It contains:
   (a) Subcutaneous muscles in the face, neck and scrotum
   (b) Mammary gland
   (c) Deeply situated sweat glands
   (d) Localized groups of lymph nodes
   (e) Cutaneous nerves and vessels.

Functions

1. Superficial fascia facilitates movements of the skin.
2. It serves as a soft medium for the passage of the vessels and nerves to the skin.
3. It conserves body heat because fat is a bad conductor of heat.

DEEP FASCIA

Definition

Deep fascia is a fibrous sheet which invests the body beneath the superficial fascia. It is devoid of fat, and is usually inelastic and tough (Fig. 8.9).

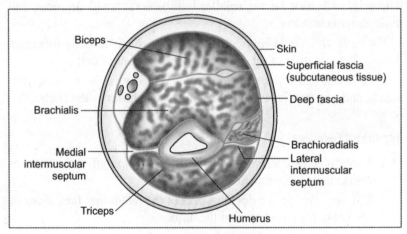

Fig. 8.9. Cross-section of an arm showing the arrangement of superficial and deep fascia.

Distribution

1. Deep fascia is *best defined* in the limbs where it forms tough and tight sleeves, and in the neck where it forms a collar.
2. It is *ill-defined* on the trunk and face.

Important Features

1. *Extensions (prolongations)* of the deep fascia form:
   (a) The intermuscular septa which divide the limb into compartments (Fig. 8.10).
   (b) The fibroareolar sheaths for the muscles, vessels and nerves.
2. *Thickenings* of the deep fascia form:
   (a) Retinacula (retention bands) around certain joints like (Fig. 8.11) wrist and ankle.

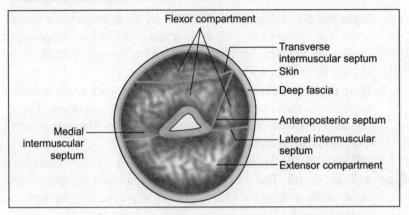

Fig. 8.10: Intermuscular septa forming compartments

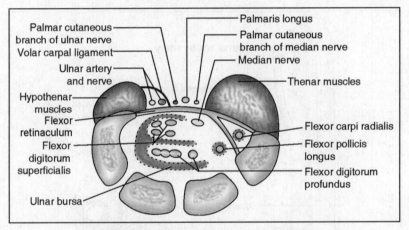

Fig. 8.11: Flexor reticulum at the wrist

   (b) The palmar and plantar aponeuroses for protection of nerves
       and blood vessels.
3. *Interruptions* in the deep fascia on the subcutaneous bones.
   Deep fascia never crosses a subcutaneous bone. Instead it blends
   with its periosteum and is bound down to the bone.

Modifications of deep fascia

   1. Forms the intermuscular septa separating functionally different
      group of muscles into separate compartments (Fig. 8.10).
   2. Covers each muscle as *epimysium* which sends in the septa to
      enclose each muscle fasciculus known as *perimysium*. From the
      perimysium septa pass to enclose each muscle fibre. These fine

septa are the *endomysium*. Through all these connective tissue septa, e.g. epimysium, perimysium and endomysium, arterioles, capillaries, venules, lymphatics and nerves traverse to reach each muscle fibre (Fig. 4.6).

3. Deep fascia covers each nerve as *epineurium*, each nerve fascicle as *perineurium* and individual nerve fibre as *endoneurium*. These connective tissue coverings support the nerve fibres and carry capillaries and lymphatics (Fig. 7.10).

4. Forms sheaths around large arteries, e.g., carotid sheath, axillary sheath. The deep fascia is dense around the artery and rather loose around the vein to give an allowance for the vein to distend (Fig. 8.12).

Fig. 8.12: Carotid sheath: **(a)** Longitudinal section, **(b)** transverse section

5. Modified to form the capsule, synovial membrane and bursae in relation to the joints.

6. Forms tendon sheaths wherever tendons cross over a joint. This mechanism prevents wear and tear of the tendon (Fig. 8.13).

7. In the region of palm and sole it is modified to form aponeuroses, e.g. palmar and plantar aponeuroses which afford protection to the underlying-structures (Fig. 8.14). It also forms septa between various muscles. These septa are specially well developed in the

calf muscles of lower limb. The contraction of calf muscles in the tight sleeve of deep fascia helps in pushing the venous blood and lymph towards the heart.

Thus the deep fascia helps in venous and lymphatic return from the lower limb (Fig. 8.15).

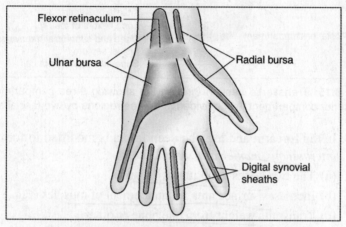

Fig. 8.13: Tendon sheaths or bursae in the palm

Fig. 8.14: Plantar aponeurosis

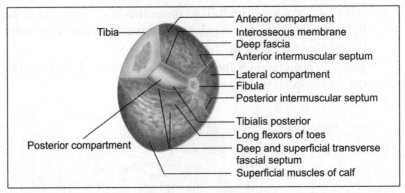

Fig. 8.15: Transverse section through leg showing three compartments. Posterior compartment is subdivided into three regions by two fascial septa

8. In the forearm and leg, the deep fascia is modified to form the *interosseous membrane*, which keeps:
   (a) The two bones at optimum distance.
   (b) Increases surface area for attachment of muscles (Fig. 8.16).
   (c) Transmits weight from one bone to other.

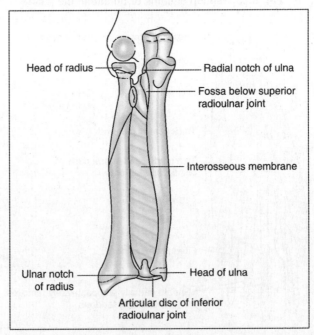

Fig. 8.16: Interosseous membrane of the forearm

Functions

1. Deep fascia keeps the underlying structures in position and preserves the characteristic surface contour of the limbs and neck.
2. It provides extra surface for muscular attachments.
3. It helps in venous and lymphatic return.
4. It assists muscles in their action by the degree of tension and pressure it exerts upon their surfaces.
5. The retinacula act as pulleys and serve to prevent the loss of power. In such situations the friction is minimized by the synovial sheaths of the tendons.

CLINICAL ANATOMY

Skin is the outer garment of the body and is subjected to following maladies.

- **Dermatitis or eczema:** There is redness, swelling, itching and exudation in acute cases. It usually becomes chronic. Dermatitis may be allergic due to soaps and cosmetics.
- **Albinism:** There is no melanin pigment. It is usually an inherited condition.
- **Herpes zoster virus:** This virus causes vesicular lesion around the nasal and oral orifices and along a dermatome. It is also responsible for causing chicken pox (Fig. 7.26).
- **Pressure sores:** The skin slowly dies over the pressure sites, e.g. pressure sores in the lower back when patient lies on the back for prolonged periods due to illness (Fig. 7.23).
- **Burns:** It is a condition which occurs due to too much heat or cold acids, alkalies and electricity, etc. If only epidermis is affected, the burn is called *superficial*. If both dermis and epidermis are affected the burn is called *deep*. Burn results in dehydration, shock and contractures.
- **Benign pigmented naevus or mole:** Melanin pigment cells are found in small numbers in the basal layer of skin. These neuroectodermal cells may proliferate at the dermoepidermal junction, in the dermis, to form naevi of different sizes and forms.
- **Colour:** Skin is pale in anaemia, yellow in jaundice and blue in cyanosis.

- **Boil (furuncle):** Boil is an infection and suppuration of the hair follicle and the sebaceous gland.
- **Skin incisions:** These should be made parallel to the lines of cleavage. This will result in small scars (Fig. 8.3).
- **Sebaceous cyst** is common in the scalp. It is due to obstruction of the duct of a sebaceous gland, caused either by trauma or infection (Fig. 8.17). If the duct of sebaceous gland of cheek is blocked, it leads to closed comedones or acne (Fig. 8.18). If the condition gets severe, the condition is acne vulgaris (Fig. 8.19).
- **Scabies** is a mite infection. It is commonly seen in genital region (Fig. 8.20) and in interdigital cleft (Fig. 8.21).

Fig. 8.17: Sebaceous cysts on the scalp

Fig. 8.18: Comedones or acne on the cheek

Fig. 8.19: Acne vulgaris

Fig. 8.20: Scabies in genital region

Fig. 8.21: Scabies in interdigital cleft

- **Keloid** is overgrowth of connective tissue at site of injury or burn (Fig. 8.22).
- **Fungal infection of nail** is common (Fig. 8.23). It may occur in between the toes also.

Fig. 8.22: Keloid after burns

Fig. 8.23: Fungal infection of the nail

- **Vitiligo** is an autoimmune disease leading to white patches on skin (Fig. 8.24).
- **Baldness** is related to hormones. Alopecia areata (Fig. 8.25) is an autoimmune disease.
- Deep fascia of the leg helps in **venous return** from the legs. The muscular contractions press on the deep veins and form an effective mechanism of venous return. This contraction becomes more effective within the tight sleeve of deep fascia.

Fig. 8.24: Vitiligo on the skin of hands

Fig. 8.25: Alopecia areata

- **Planes:** The deep fascia forms planes and the fluid or pus tracks along these fascial planes. The tubercular abscess of the cervical vertebrae passes along the prevertebral fascia into the posterior triangle of neck or into the axilla.
- **Retinacula** keep the tendons and nerves in position. Sometimes the delicate nerve may get compressed as it traverses under the retinacula. Median nerve may get compressed deep to the flexor retinaculum, leading to the *Carpal tunnel syndrome* (Fig. 8.11).
- Similarly tibial nerve may get compressed under the flexor retinaculum of leg leading to *Tarsal tunnel syndrome*.

(Figures 8.18 to 8.25 have kindly been provided by Dr. Anuradha and Dr. Praveen Aggarwal of Aggarwal Medical Centre, Naveen Shahdara, Delhi)

9 Connective Tissue, Ligaments and Raphe

CONNECTIVE TISSUE

Introduction

Connective tissue is a widely distributed general type of tissue which supports, binds and protects the special (well differentiated) tissues of the body.

It has both the cellular and extracellular components.

The cellular component of connective tissue plays the role of active defence, whereas the extracellular component (fibres and ground substance) serves a number of mechanical functions of support and protection against the mechanical stresses and strains.

The ordinary type of connective tissue is distributed all over the body, but the special type of connective tissue forms certain well differentiated tissues, like the bone and cartilage.

A number of cell types of the connective tissue are also found in the blood and lymph.

The greater part of connective tissue develops from embryonic mesoderm.

The cells of the connective tissue are widely separated by the abundance of extracellular matrix.

CONSTITUENT ELEMENTS

Connective tissue is made up of cells and extracellular matrix.

A. Cells

Cells are fibroblast, macrophage, plasma cell, mast cell, fat cell, and pigment cell.

B. Extracellular Matrix

The matrix has a fibrous and a non-fibrous element. The fibrous element has three types of fibres — collagen, elastin and reticulin. The non-fibrous element is formed by the ground substance.

TYPES OF CONNECTIVE TISSUE

Different types of connective tissue are found in different parts of the body according to the local functional requirements. These types are based on predominance of the cell type, concentration and arrangement of the fibre type, and character of ground substance. The connective tissues are classified as follows.

I. Loose Connective Tissue

Its types are: Areolar tissue, adipose tissue, myxomatous tissue and reticular tissue. These are described in Garg, Kaul, Bahl: *A Textbook of Histology—A Colour Atlas and Text*, 4 edn, CBS Publishers & Distributors, New Delhi.

II. Dense Irregular Connective Tissue

1. Ordinary - tendon
2. Specialised - cartilage and bone which have been described in Chapter 2.

Functions of Connective Tissue

1. As a packing material, connective tissue provides a *supporting matrix* for many highly organized structures.
2. It forms *restraining mechanism* of the body in the form of retinacula, check ligaments (Fig. 9.1) and fibrous pulley (Fig. 9.2).
3. The ensheathing layer of *deep fascia* preserves the characteristic contour of the limbs and aids circulation in the veins and lymphatics (Fig. 5.8).
4. It provides surface coating of the body in the form of *superficial fascia* which stores fat and conserves body heat.
5. It provides *additional surface* for the attachment of muscles in the form of deep fascia, intermuscular septa and interosseous membranes (Figs 8.15, 8.16).

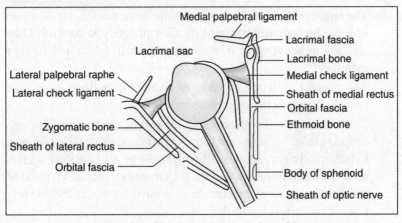

Fig. 9.1: Check ligaments in the orbit

Fig. 9.2: Fibrous pulley to change the direction of muscle

6. It forms *fascial planes* which provide convenient pathways for vessels (blood vessels and lymphatics) and nerves.

7. In places where it is loose in texture (loose connective tissue) it *facilitates movements* between the adjacent structures, and by forming bursal sacs it minimizes friction and pressure effects (Fig. 8.13).

8. Connective tissue helps in the *repair of injuries* whereby the fibroblasts lay down collagen fibres to form the scar tissue.

9. The *macrophages* of connective tissue serve a defensive function against the bacterial invasion by their phagocytic activity. They also act as scavengers in removing the cell debris and foreign material.

   The *plasma cells* are capable of producing antibodies against specific antigens (foreign proteins).

   The *mast cells,* by producing histamine and serotonin, are responsible for the various inflammatory, allergic and hypersensitivity reactions. *Pigment cells* protect the skin against ultraviolet radiation, so that the inflammatory changes typical of sunburn do not occur, and the chromosomal damage in the dividing cells of epidermis is avoided.

10. Connective tissue contains mesenchymal cells of embryonic type. These are capable of transformation into each type of the connective tissue cells with their discrete functions.

LIGAMENTS

Definition

Ligaments are fibrous bands which connect the adjacent bones, forming integral parts of the joints. They are tough and unyielding, but at the same time are flexible and pliant, so that the normal movements can occur without any resistance, but the abnormal movements are prevented.

Types of Ligaments

A. According to their composition
1. Most of the ligaments are made up of collagen fibres. These are inelastic and unstretchable (Fig. 9.3).
2. A few ligaments, like the ligamenta flava and ligaments of auditory ossicles, are made up of elastin fibres (predominantly). These are elastic and stretchable (Fig. 9.4).

B. According to their relation to the joint
1. Intrinsic ligaments surround the joint, and may be extracapsular or intracapsular.
2. Extrinsic ligaments are independent of the joint; and lie away from it (Fig. 9.5).

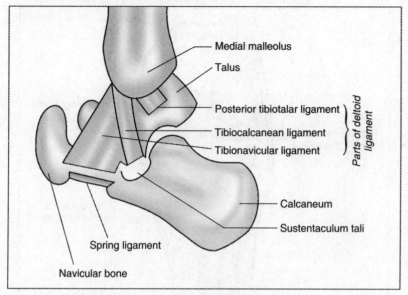

Fig. 9.3: Collagenous, deltoid ligament

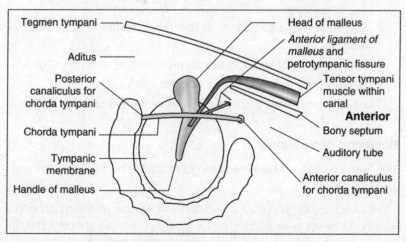

Fig. 9.4: Elastin, anterior ligament of malleus

Morphology

Ligaments are usually considered as degenerated tendons of the related muscles.

1. Tibial collateral ligament is degenerated tendon of adductor magnus muscle.

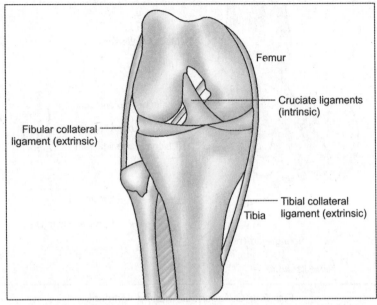

Fig. 9.5: Some of the extrinsic and intrinsic ligaments of knee joint

2. Sacrotuberous ligament is degenerated tendon of long head of biceps femoris.
3. Sacrospinous ligament is degenerated part of coccygeus muscle.
4. Long plantar ligament is part of peroneus longus.

Their tendinous nature is evident in some animal ancestors.

Blood and Nerve Supply

The blood vessels and nerves of the joint ramify on its ligaments and supply them.

Most ligaments serve as sense organs because of their rich nerve supply. They act as important reflex mechanisms and are important in monitoring the position and movements of the joint.

Functions

1. Ligaments are important agents in maintaining the stability at the joint.
2. Their sensory function makes them important reflex organs, so that their joint stabilizing role is far more efficient.

RAPHE

A raphe is a linear fibrous band formed by interdigitation of the tendinous or aponeurotic ends of the muscles. It differs from a ligament in that it is *stretchable*.

Examples: linea alba, pterygomandibular raphe, mylohyoid raphe, median pharyngeal raphe (Fig. 9.6), anococcygeal raphe, etc.

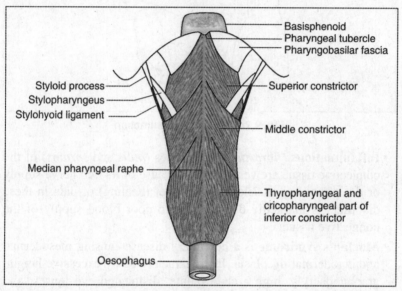

Fig. 9.6

CLINICAL ANATOMY OF CONNECTIVE TISSUE

- *Collagen diseases* include rheumatic fever, rheumatoid arthritis, disseminated lupus erythematosus, scleroderma, dermatomyositis, polyarteritis nodosa, and serum sickness. These are the diseases of connective tissue characterized by its fibrinoid necrosis.
- **Scleroderma** is a slowly progressive rheumatic disease accompanied by vascular lesions, especially in the skin, lungs and kidneys. It is characterized by deposition of fibrous tissue in the skin. This leads to thickness and firmness of the affected areas. It is a autoimmune disease of connective tissue.

- **Dupuytren's contracture:** Occurs due to contraction of fibrous tissue of palmar aponeurosis. The disease results in flexion deformities of fingers, especially ring finger and little finger (Fig. 9.7).

Fig. 9.7: Dupuytren's contracture

- **Inflammations** *(fibrositis)* and injuries *(pulls* and *sprains)* of the connective tissue are very painful because of its rich nerve supply or the associated muscle spasm. Relief (healing) of pain in these disorders is markedly delayed due to poor blood supply of the connective tissue.
- **Marfan's syndrome** is a hereditary disease causing mesodermal and ectodermal dysplasia. It is characterized by excessive height, arachnodactyly, high arched palate, dislocated eye lenses, and congenital heart disease.
- Tendons at the back of wrist are enveloped by synovial sheath. At times the sheath may form a swelling at back of wrist. This is called the "simple ganglion" (Fig. 9.8).

Fig. 9.8: Ganglion at the back of wrist

Ganglion is a cystic swelling resulting from mucoid degeneration of synovial sheaths around the tendons.

CLINICAL ANATOMY OF LIGAMENTS

- Undue stretching and tearing of the fibres of a ligament due to an injury is known as 'sprain'. It causes severe pain and effusion into the ligament and joint. The bones are normal as seen in the X-ray film.
- The joint stability is lost in the neuropathic joints, as occurs in tabes dorsalis, syringomyelia, leprosy, etc.

X-ray skull showing frontal and maxillary air sinuses

Dens of axis, seen through the open mouth

10 Principles of Radiography

X-ray are a kind of electromagnetic waves which are used extensively in medicine for both diagnostic and therapeutic purposes.

All *electromagnetic waves* (X-rays, ultraviolet rays, infrared rays and radio waves) are produced by acceleration of electrons.

HISTORICAL

X-rays were discovered accidentally on November 8, 1895, by Wilhelm Konrad Roentgen.

Roentgen was a German physicist from the University of Wurzburg. He was engaged in studying the behaviour of an electron beam when passed through a vacuum to strike a tungsten plate. To his surprise, he observed that, in addition to electrons, certain unknown rays were also produced, which could pass through the glass envelope of his apparatus and caused a glow on a distant fluorescent screen. He was able to photograph the bones of his hand by placing the hand over a photographic plate and then shining the rays on it. For his unique discovery, Roentgen was awarded the first Nobel Prize in Physics in 1901.

The discovery of X-rays provided a new dimension to the advancement of medical and other sciences.

The medical uses of X-rays are both diagnostic and therapeutic.

As a diagnostic tool, radiography has proved of great value in detection of the early stages of deep-seated diseases, when the possibility of cure is greatest.

Therapeutically, X-rays (radiotherapy) are used in the treatment of cancer (selected cases) because, the rays can destroy cancer cells much more easily without destroying the adjacent normal cells.

PROPERTIES OF X-RAYS

The relevant properties of X-rays are as follows.

1. Penetrating Power

X-rays form a part of the spectrum of electromagnetic radiation. They closely resemble the visible lightrays in having a similar photographic effect. But they differ from the lightrays in being invisible and in having a shorter wavelength. The wavelength of X-rays is 1/10,000 of that of the light rays, i.e. $7.5 \times 10^{-6} - 1.71 \times 10^{-9}$ cm. It is this property of shorter wavelength which gives them the power of penetration of different materials.

When X-rays pass through the matter, the rays are absorbed to varying extents. The degree of absorption depends on the density (atomic weight) of the matter. Radiography is based on the differential absorption of the X-rays. Dense tissues, like the bone, absorb X-rays far more readily than do the soft tissues of the body. Structures which are easily penetrated by the X-rays are described as *radiolucent,* and the structures which are penetrated with difficulty or are not penetrated at all are described as *radiopaque.*

The various structures can be arranged in a scale of increasing radiopacity.

(a) Air, in the respiratory passages, stomach and intestines.

(b) Fat.

(c) Soft tissues, e.g. muscles, vessels, nerves, and viscera.

(d) Bones, due to their calcium content.

(e) Enamel of teeth, and

(f) Dense foreign bodies, e.g. metallic fillings in the teeth, and radiopaque contrast media.

2. Photographic Effect

When X-rays strike a photosensitive film, the film gets photosensitized. When such a film is developed and fixed chemically, a radiography image is obtained.

X-ray film is made up of cellulose acetate, which is coated on its both sides with silver bromide (photosensitive) emulsion 0.001 inch thick. The film is blue tinted and transparent.

An X-ray image (picture) is called skiagram (skia = shadow), radiograph, or roentgenogram. Radiolucent structures produce black shadows and the radiopaque structures produce white shadows in the usual negative film. It is useful to remember that gas shadows are black shadows and bone shadows are the white shadows.

3. Fluorescent Effect

When X-rays strike certain metallic salts (phosphorous, zinc, cadmium, sulphide), the rays cause them to fluoresce, that is, light rays are produced. This property of X-rays is utilized in fluoroscopy.

4. Biological Effect

X-rays can destroy abnormal cells (e.g. malignant cells) much more easily than the adjacent normal cells. This property of X-rays is utilized in the treatment of various cancers.

However, X-rays are potentially dangerous. On repeated exposures, they can cause burns, tumours, and even mutations. Therefore, adequate protective measures must be taken against repeated exposures to X-rays.

RADIOGRAPHIC VIEWS

Radiographs of a part taken in more than one view give a more complete information about the entire structure by eliminating some particular overlapping shadows in particular views.

The 'view' expresses the direction of flow of the X-rays. In AP *(anteroposterior)* view the rays pass from the anterior to the posterior surface, and the posterior surface faces the X-ray plate. In PA *(posteroanterior)* view the X-rays pass from the posterior to the anterior surface, and the anterior surface faces the X-ray plate. The part of the body facing the X-ray plate (i.e. near the X-ray plate) casts a sharper shadow than the part facing the X-ray tube.

The chest skiagrams are usually taken in PA view, but for visualizing the thoracic spine, AP view is preferred.

The 'view' can also be expressed by mentioning the surface facing the X-ray plate. Thus AP view can also be called as *posterior* view, and the PA view as the *anterior* view.

Similarly, when right surface of the body faces the plate, it is called the *right lateral* view, and when the left surface of the body faces the plate it is called the *left lateral* view.

Oblique and other special views are taken to visualize certain special structures.

RADIOGRAPHIC PROCEDURES

1. Fluoroscopy

Fluoroscopy is of special advantage in observing the movements of the organs (lungs, stomach, intestines, etc.), and in changing the position of the subject during the examination.

Fluoroscopy is done in a dark room.

The fluoroscopic image is visualized directly on the fluorescent screen which is covered with a sheet of lead glass to absorb the X-rays and to protect the fluoroscopist.

The sharpness of the fluoroscopic image is inferior to that of a radiograph.

Fluoroscopic image is photographed by a camera in mass miniature radiography (MMR) by which the masses can be surveyed for the detection of diseases such as tuberculosis.

2. Plain Radiography

A natural X-ray image, obtained directly without using any contrast medium, is called a *plain skiagram* or a *plain radiograph*. Plain radiography is particularly useful in the study of normal and abnormal bones, lungs, paranasal air sinuses and gaseous shadows in the abdomen (Fig. 10.1).

3. Contrast Radiography

The various hollow viscera and body cavities cannot be visualized in plain radiographs due to their poor differential radiopacity. However, their contrast can be accentuated by filling such organs or cavities with either a radiopaque or a radiolucent substance. Radiography done after artificial accentuation of the contrast is called *contrast radiography* .

The radiopaque compounds used in *contrast radiography* are:

1. Barium sulphate suspension (emulsion) in water for gastrointestinal tract (Fig. 10.2).

Fig. 10.1: Plain radiography of abdomen

Fig. 10.2: The stomach and small intestine visualised by barium meal

2. The aqueous solution of appropriate iodine compounds, for urinary and biliary passages and the vascular system.

Special Procedures

1. **Computerized tomography (CT scanning):** Computerized tomography is a major technological breakthrough in radiology, especially neuroradiology (Fig. 10.3).

   It provides images comparable to anatomical slices (3–6 mm thick) of the brain, in which one can distinguish tissues with even slight differences in their radiodensity, viz. CSF, blood, white and grey matter, and the neoplasms.

   Differentiation between vascular and avascular areas can be enhanced by simultaneous injection of a radiopaque medium in the vessels.

   Thus CT scanning helps in the diagnosis of the exact location and size of the tumours, haemorrhage, infarction and malformations, including hydrocephalus, cerebral atrophy, etc.

   This technique is also called as CAT (computerized axial tomography) scanning because it provides images in transverse, or axial plane.

Fig. 10.3: CT scan of the thorax

2. **Ultrasonograph:** Ultrasonic diagnostic echography is a safe procedure because instead of X-rays the high frequency sound waves are used. These sound waves are reflected by the acoustic

interface (different tissues) back to their source and are recorded in a polarised camera.

The sound waves used are above the range of human hearing, i.e. above 20,000 cycles per second, or 20 kilohertz (hertz = cycles per second). As the technique is quite safe, it is especially valuable in obstetric and gynaecological problems. Figures 10.4 and 10.5 show the ultrasound of the neck and thyroid gland

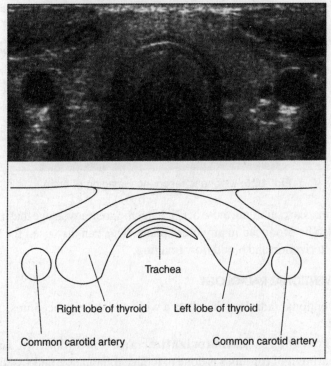

Fig. 10.4: Ultrasound of the neck and thyroid gland

MAGNETIC RESONANCE IMAGING

The MRI uses a strong magnet and pulses of radiowaves. A pulse of radiowaves of the appropriate frequency displaces hydrogen nuclei from their new alignment. They return to their position immediately after the pulse ceases. At the same time they release the energy absorbed as a radio signal of the same frequency which is detected. The signal returned is proportional to the concentration of the protons. This is converted by computer into an analogue image presented on a screen. MRI can produce

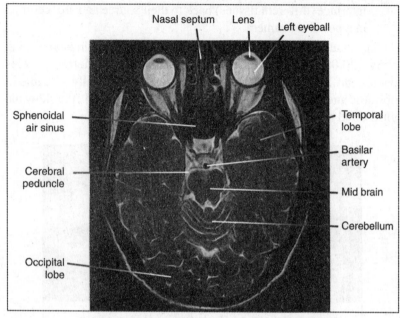

Fig. 10.5: Magnetic resonance imaging of brain.

axial images resembling those of CT. It has the great advantage that images can also be produced in any other plane. This can also used for tissue characterization and blood flow imaging.

INTERVENTIONAL RADIOLOGY

Interventional radiology involves a wide variety of procedures. These include:

- **Percutaneous catheterization and embolisation in the treatment of tumours** is done to reduce tumour size and vascularity prior to operation in difficult cases.
- **Percutaneous transluminal dilatation and arterial stenosis** for the treatment of localized stenosis in the arteries.
- **Needle biopsy under imaging control** for lung tumours and abdominal masses.
- **Transhepatic catheterization of the bile ducts** for draining in obstructive jaundice.
- **Needle puncture and drainage of cysts in the kidney** or other organs using control by simple X-ray or ultrasound.

Anatomical Word Meanings and Historical Names

A	Anglo-Saxon	E	English	It	Italian
Ar	Arabic	F	French	L	Latin
C	Chinese	G	Greek	S	Sanskrit
Du	Dutch	Gr	German		

	Afferent	coming towards
	Anus	ring
(G)	Artery	blood vessel
(L)	Articulation	joint
(G)	Arytenoid	like a pitcher
(G)	Ascites	bag-like (fluid collection)
	Astrocyte	star-shaped
	Atavism	a remote ancestor (epiphysis)
	Atelectasis	incomplete expansion
	Atheroma	tumour
	Atlas	carry earth on head — 1st cervical vertebra
	Atresia	no hole
(L)	Atrium	central open part
(G)	Atrophy	ill-nourished
(L)	Auditory	related to hearing
	Auerbach (German anatomist)	Auerbach's plexus of autonomic nerves between longitudinal and circular coats of gastrointestinal tract
(L)	Auricle	diminutive of ear
	Auscultation	to hear with attention
	Autonomic	self-controller
(G)	Autopsy	self-seeing
(L)	Avulsion	to tear away
(L)	Axilla	armpit
(L)	Axis	carry (pillar)—2nd cervical vertebra

(G)	Azygous	unpaired—azygous vein in thorax
(F)	Ballotment	tossing
	Basilic	medial vein of arm
	Basophilic	basic stain of nucleus
(L)	Bile	fluid
	Biliverdin	green bile
	Bilirubin	red bile
(G)	Bio	life
	Birth	bearing of offspring
(A)	Bladder	watery swelling
(G)	Blepharitis	eyelid inflammation
(L)	Bolus	mass
(A)	Bone	bar
(F)	Boss	a hump
(G)	Botany	grass
	Bowman	Bowman's capsule, Bowman's memb,
	(English surgeon)	Bowman's muscle of ciliary body
(L)	Brachium	arm
(G)	Brady	slow
(G)	Brain	upper part of head
(G)	Branchia	gills of fishes - branchial arches
(A)	Breast	bursting forth
(A)	Breech	lower part of trunk and thigh
(G)	Bregma	forepart of head
	Brown-Séquard	Brown-Séquard syndrome - hemisection of
	(British neurologist)	spinal cord
	Broca	Broca's area - speech centre
	(French surgeon)	
(G)	Bronchus	windpipe
(G)	Bronchiole	terminal air tube
(F)	Bruise	to break
	Brunner	Brunner's duodenal glands
	(Swiss anatomist)	
(L)	Bucia	cheek
(L)	Buccinator	trumpeter
(E)	Buffer	cushion to soften blow
(L)	Bulb	as onion
(L)	Bulbar	medulla oblongata
(L)	Bulbocavernosus	
	or	
(L)	Bulbospongiosus	accelerator of urine
(L)	Bulla	bubble

(It)	Bunion	swelling
(G)	Burdach (Greek anatomist)	post. column of spinal cord
	Bursa	a purse
(E)	Buttock	end (prominence post. to hip)
(L)	Cadaver	a dead body
(L)	Caecum	blind
	Cesarean section (Julius Caesar was born)	cutting uterus for taking out a baby
(F)	Caisson	box
	Cajal (Spanish histologist)	Cajal stain
(L)	Calamine	red
(L)	Calculus	little stone
(L)	Calvaria	vault of cranium
(L)	Calcaneus	bone of foot
(L)	Calcar	spur (calcarine sulcus)
(L)	Calcar femorale	strong plate of bone in front of lesser trochanter supporting neck of femur (spur-shaped)
(L)	Calcarine fissure	spur-shaped
	Calcination	to make bone
	Calyx	covering of bud/shell
	Calveria	vault
	Camper (Dutch anatomist)	superficial fascia of anterior abdominal wall
(L)	Canal	channel or furrow
	Canal of Arnold	for lesser petrosal nerve
	Canal of Schlemm	at cornea-scleral junction
(L)	Cancellous	lattice work
(L)	Cancer	crab-like
(L)	Canine	related to dog (teeth)
	Cannula	hollow, tubular instrument
(L)	Capillary	like hair of head (caput), fine tube
	Capsule	a small box
(L)	Caput	head
	Capitulum	in humerus (lateral part of lower end)
	Caput Medusae	(head of witch) seen because of dilatation of veins at umbilicus due to cirrhosis of liver
(L)	Carbohydrate	made of carbon, hydrogen and water
	Caput succedaneum	swelling produced on presenting part of fetal head during labour
(G)	Cardia	heart

(L)	Caries	decay of bone and teeth
(L)	Carina	structure with a projecting central ridge
(L)	Caro	flesh
(G)	Carotid	to throttle (blood vessel)
	Carotid tubercle	ant. tubercle of 6th cervical vertebra
(L)	Carpus	wrist
(L)	Cartilage	gristle
(L)	Castrate	to cut off
(G)	Catarrh	to flow down
	Catgut	from intestine of sheep
(L)	Cauda	tail
	Caudate	Caudate nucleus, Caudate lobe (tail-shaped)
(E)	Caul	cap (fetal membrane with fluid)
(G)	Causalgia	burning pain
(L)	Cavernous	full of compartments
(L)	Cell	small room
	Cement	binding
	Centrifuge	fleeing away from centre
(G)	Centrosome	body centre
(G)	Cephalic	to head (cephalic vein)
(L)	Cera	wax
(L)	Cerebellum	little brain
(L)	Cerebrum	brain
(L)	Cerumen	ear wax
(L)	Cervix	neck, e.g. cervix of uterus, cervical rib
(G)	Chancre	venereal disease
	Chemotaxis	reaction of living cells to chemical agents
	Chest	box
(G)	Chiasma	crossing over
(G)	Chitin	coat
(G)	Chole	bile
(G)	Cholesterin	solid bile
(G)	Chord	a cord of string, e.g. chorda tympani nerve
	Chordata	animals with notochord
(G)	Chorea	dancing (disease of basal gang)
(G)	Chorion	skin
(G)	Chromosome	coloured bodies
(G)	Chyme	juice
	Cilium	eyelid
(L)	Cingulum	girdle
(L)	Circle of Haller	venous circle in areola of female breast
(L)	Circular sinus	sinus around pituitary
	Circle of Willis	arterial circle at base of brain

(L)	Circulation	motion in circle
(L)	Circum	around, e.g. circumflex artery
	Cirrhosis	to turn reddish yellow
	Cisterna	reservoir (at base of brain)
(L)	Claustrum	barrier
	Clavicle	diminutive of key
	Cledio	closes the thorax, clavipectoral fascia
(G)	Climacteric	step of a stair (menopause)
	Clinic	at the bed side
	Clinoid	surround pituitary fossa like four posts of bed
(G)	Clitoris	tender (female external genitalia)
(L)	Clivus	slope of a hill - part of cranial fossae
(L)	Cloaca	drain or sewer (dilated part of hindgut)
(G)	Clonus	confused motion
(L)	Coagulation	to curdle
(L)	Coarctation	to press together (coarctation of aorta)
(G)	Coccyx	cuckoo (coccyx resembles bill of a cuckoo) - lowest part of vertebral column
(L)	Cochlea	snail (internal ear)
(G)	Coelenterate	hollow (internal)
(G)	Coeliac	belly (c. axis artery for stomach)
(G)	Coelome	hollow
	Cohnheim (scientist)	Cohnheim's areas in skeletal muscle
	Colic	pain in intestine
(G)	Collagen	glue producing substance
	Colloidion	glue-like
	Colon	large intestine
	Colostrum	first milk secreted by breasts
	Colpotomy	cutting through vagina
(L)	Commissure	join together
(L)	Complement	I fill up
(L)	Concha	shell (in lat. wall of nose)
(L)	Concussion	a shaking
(G)	Condyle	knob formed by knuclle of any joint
(L)	Conjugate	yoked together
(L)	Conjunctiva	mucus membrane of eye
(L)	Conus	cone
(G)	Coracoid	a crow-like process of scapula
(L)	Corneum	most superficial layer of epithelium of skin
(G)	Corona	crown, e.g. corona radiata and coronal suture corona glandis (coronary arteries, coronary sulcus)
(L)	Corpus	body, e.g. corpus callosum, corpus luteum

(L)	Corpuscle	a little body, pacinian corpuscle, thymic corpuscle
(L)	Corrugator	wrinkler
(L)	Cortex	outer bark (grey matter)
(L)	Cortex	rind (outer layer)
(L)	Costa	rib
(A)	Cough	violent expulsion
	Cowper	Cowper's gland near upper end of male urethra
(S)	Coxa	hip
	Cramp	to contract
(L)	Cranium	skull
(G)	Creatine	(flesh) a non-protein nitrogenous substance from flesh
(G)	Cremaster	a suspender (of testis)
	Crepitus	a little noise
(L)	Creta	a chalk ($CaCO_3$)
(F)	Cretin	congenital myxoedema
(L)	Cribriform	sieve-like, e.g. cribiform fascia of thigh
(G)	Cricoid	ring, e.g. cricoid cartilage
(L)	Crista	crest
	Crista galli	cock's comb
(L)	Crus	shin bone or leg
(L)	Crural	leg
(L)	Cruciate	cross-like
(L)	Crypt	underground vault (hidden)
(G)	Crystal	clear ice
(L)	Cubitus	elbow
(G)	Cuboid	cube-like
(L)	Culture	growth
(L)	Cuneiform	wedge-shaped
	Cupola	dome-shaped
(L)	Curriculum	a course of study
(L)	Cusp	point of a spear (cusp of valve)
(L)	Cutis	skin
(F)	Cuvier (anatomist)	ducts of Cuvier
(G)	Cyclops	one-eyed giant
(L)	Cyst	bladder, cystic duct
	Cytoplasm	spread outside the nucleus
(G)	Dacryocyte	tear-drop
(G)	Dactylitis	finger inflammation
	Dale (English physician)	histamine discovered by Dale
(E)	Dandruff	skin scabs

(S)	Dartos	leather
	Darwin tubercle	projection in upper part of ear
(L)	Decalcify	process which extracts Ca^{++}
(L)	Deci	one tenth
(L)	Deciduous	falling off
	Decompression	decreased pressure
(L)	Decubitus	lying down
(L)	Decussate	intersection of two lines
(L)	Defecate	to evacuate the bowels
(L)	Degenerate	structural impairment of a tissue
(L)	Deglutition	action of swallowing
	Deiters (German anatomist)	Deiters cells in internal ear
(G)	Deltoid	triangular in shape, deltoid muscle, deltoid ligament
(L)	Dementia	to be mad
(F)	Demilune	half moon, demilune of Giannuzzi
(G)	Dendron	tree, dendrites of neuron
	Denonvilliers (French surgeon)	fascia between rectum and prostate is Denonvilliers' fascia
(L)	Dens	tooth-like dens of 2nd vertebra/axis
(L)	Dentate	tooth-like, dentate lig. of pia mater, dentate gyrus of brain
(Gr)	Dermis	skin
	Descemet (French surgeon)	Descemet's membrane of cornea
(L)	Desquamate	to scale off
(L)	Detrusor	to thrust away, detrusor muscle of urinary bladder
(L)	Dexter	right
(G)	Diagnosis	thro knowledge
(G)	Dialysis	to loose from one another
(G)	Diapedesis	leading through
(G)	Diaphragm	a partition
(G)	Diaphysis	growing through
(G)	Diarrhoea	flowing through
(G)	Diarthrosis	joint
(G)	Diastole	a pause
(G)	Diathermy	very hot
(G)	Dichotomous	cut in half
(G)	Didelphys	double uterus
(G)	Diencephalon	between brain
(G)	Diet	a way of living

(G)	Digastric	double belly
(L)	Digestion	to dissolve
(L)	Digit	finger
(G)	Diphtheria	leather-like membrane
(G)	Diploë	double layers (deiploë of some of the skull bones)
(F)	Disease	not well
(L)	Dislocation	pulled out of place
(L)	Dissect	cut apart
(G)	Diuresis	increased urination
(L)	Diverticulum	a small cul-de-sac
(L)	Doctor	a teacher and a healer
(G)	Dolichocephalic	long head
(L)	Dorsum	back
(It)	Douche	to pour
	Douglas (Scottish anatomist)	pouch of Douglas (rectouterine pouch)
(L)	Duct	to conduct
(L)	Duodenum	width of 12 fingers
	Dupuytren (French surgeon)	Dupuytren's contracture
(L)	Duramater	hard mother
(G)	Dys (prefix)	bad, e.g. dysentery, dyspepsia, dysmenorrhoea
(G)	Ectoderm	outside skin
(G)	Ectopia	displacement (out of place)
(G)	Ectropion	to turn from
(G)	Eczema	anything thrown out by heat
	Edinger (German anatomist)	Edinger-Westphal nuclei of III N
	Effector	to effect
(L)	Efferent	going away
(L)	Element	a rudiment
(G)	Elephantiasis	elephant-like legs
(G)	Embed	holding in place
(G)	Embolus	a plug
(G)	Embryo	something that grows in another's body
(G)	Emesis	vomiting
(L)	Emissary	escape channels (emissary veins connecting intracranial sinuses with extracranial veins)
(L)	Empirical	experienced, not scientific
(L)	Emulsion	milk-like mixture
(F)	Enamel	coating on metal

(F)	Enarthrosis	ball and socket joint
(G)	Encephalon	brain plus head
(G)	Endarteritis	blockage within arteries
(G)	Endemic	native
(G)	Endo (prefix)	within, e.g. endocrine, endolymph, endometrium, endothelium
(G)	Enema	to inject
(L)	Ensiform	sword-like, xiphoid process
(G)	Enteric	gut
(G)	Enuresis	urine passed
(G)	Enzyme	which causes fermentation
(G)	Eosin	pink
(G)	Ependyma	wrap
(G)	Epicondyle	upon a knob
(G)	Epicranius	upon head
(G)	Epicritic	fine touch
(G)	Epidermis	upon dermis
(G)	Epididymis	upon testis
(G)	Epigastrium	upon belly
(G)	Epiglottis	upon tongue
(G)	Epihyal	part of 2nd arch
(G)	Epilepsy	a seizure
(G)	Epinephrine	hormone
(G)	Epiploic	omental
(G)	Episiotomy	cutting the pudendum (perineum)
(G)	Epispadius	upon a tear
(G)	Epistaxis	to trickle
(G)	Epithelium	upon nipple
(G)	Epoophoron	upon egg-bearing
	Erb (German neurologist)	Erb's palsy (C 5, 6)
(L)	Erector	to stand up
(G)	Erotic	love
(L)	Eructation	throwing upwards
(G)	Ethmoid	sieve-like
(G)	Etiology	giving the cause
(G)	Etymology	true analysis of a word
(G)	Euthanasia	painless death
(L)	Eustachius (Italian anatomist)	eustachian valve
(L)	Evolution	to unroll
(G)	Exacerbation	to irritate
(L)	Exogenous	on the outside

(L)	Experiment	an active test
(L)	Extension	stretch out
(L)	Exteroceptor	outward receptor
(L)	Exude	to sweat out
(L)	Facet	a little face
(L)	Facial	related to face
	Falciform/Falx	sickle-shaped
	Fallopius (Italian anatomist)	fallopian tube
(L)	Fascia	a bandage
(L)	Fasciculus	a passage
(L)	Febris	fever
(L)	Femur	thigh
(L)	Fenestra	window
(L)	Ferment	warm
(L)	Fetus	offspring
(L)	Fibula	needle of brooch (bone)
(L)	Filament	small thread
(L)	Filaria	a thread
(L)	Fimbria	a fringe/border
(L)	Fissure	cleft
(L)	Fistula	a pipe
(L)	Flagellum	a whip
(L)	Flatus	to blow
(L)	Flavine	yellow
(L)	Flex	to bend
(L)	Flocculus	a tuft of wool
(L)	Folium	leaf
(L)	Follicle	a bag
	Fontana (Italian anatomist)	spaces of Fontana
(L)	Fontanelle	small fountain
(L)	Foramen	hole
(L)	Forensic	pertaining to law, courts - Forensic medicine
(L)	Fornix	an arch
(L)	Fossa	ditch
(L)	Fourchette	little fork
(L)	Fovea	a small pit
(L)	Frenulum	bridle, e.g. Franulum of tongue, of clitoris, of penis
(L)	Frontal	forehead
(L)	Fundus	larger part
(L)	Fundiform	sling-shaped

(L)	Funiculus	cord
(L)	Fusiform	spindle-shaped
(E)	Gag	to suffocate
	Galea	helmet, galea aponeurotica
	Galen (Roman physician)	vein of Galen, (great cerebral vein)
(A)	Gall	bile
(G)	Gamete	a married person
(G)	Ganglion	a knot
(L)	Gastric	belly
(G)	Gastrocnemius	calf of leg
(G)	Gastrula	belly
(G)	Gene	unit of heredity
	Genetics	study of natural development of race
(L)	Genial	chin
(L)	Genu	bend, knee, (genu of corpus callosum)
(G)	Genus	family
(G)	Geriatrics	study and treatment of old persons
(L)	Gustatory	sense of taste
(L)	Gyrus	convolution
(L)	Haeme	blood
	Haematoxylin	stain
(L)	Hallux	big toe
(A)	Hamstring	a little hook
	Hartman (German anatomist)	gall bladder cyst near cystic duct
(L)	Haustrum	bucket-shaped haustration of large intestine
	Havers (English physician)	haversian gland - pad of fat in joints
	Heister (German anatomist)	Heister's valve (in gall bladder)
(G)	Helicotrema	an opening between two scala of cochlea
(G)	Helix	a coil
	Helmholtz (German physician)	Helmholtz theory of color vision
	Henle (German anatomist)	Henle's loop, Henle's layer in hair follicle
	Hensen (German physician)	Hensen's node
(G)	Hepar	liver
(G)	Hermaphrodite	both sexes
(L)	Hernia	rupture
(G)	Herpes	to spread

(G)	Hetero	different
	Hilton (English surgeon)	Hilton's line
(L)	Hilum	depression
(G)	Hippocampus	sea horse
	Hirschsprung (Danish physician)	Hirschsprung's disease (congenital megacolon)
(G)	Histamine	tissue amine
(G)	Histo	anything woven
(G)	Histology	study of woven structures/tissues
(L)	Homo	a man
(G)	Hormone	to set in motion
	Horner (Swiss ophthalmologist)	Horner's syndrome
	Hunter (Scottish surgeon)	Hunter's canal (add. canal)
(G)	Hyaline	glass-like; hyaline cartilage
(G)	Hybrid	of double origin
(F)	Hydatid	a drop of water
(G)	Hydrocele	water + hernia
(G)	Hygiene	healthy
(G)	Hymen	membrane
(G)	Hyoid	U-shaped
(G)	Hyper	in excess of
	Hypnosis	state of being asleep
(G)	Hypoblast	endoderm
(G)	Hypodermic	under the skin
(G)	Hypothesis	placing under
(G)	Hyster	uterus
(G)	Icterus	a yellow bird (jaundice)
(G)	Idiopathic	'unknown'
(G)	Idiosyncrasy (allergy)	individual peculiarity
(G)	Ileum	twisted gut
(L)	Ilium	hip bone
(L)	Immunity	exemption or protection
(L)	Incise	to cut into
(L)	Incubation	to sit or brood
(L)	Incus	an anvil (ear ossicle)
(L)	Index	a pointer
(8)	Indigo	blue dye
(L)	Inducium	a tunic
	I. griesum	a grey tunic

(L)	Infant	not speaking
(L)	Infarct	necrotic
(L)	Infection	a bending inward
(L)	Inflame	to set aflame
(L)	Infra	below
(L)	Inguinal	the groin—inguinal canal
(G)	Inion	below occiput
(L)	Injection	putting in
(L)	Innominate	unnamed
(L)	Inoculate	to ingraft
(L)	Inquest	inquire
(L)	Insanity	unsound mind
(L)	Insemination	seed
(L)	In situ	manner of lying in local position
(L)	Instrument	to equip
(L)	Insufflation	to blow into
(L)	Insula	island
(L)	Internuncial	inter-messenger
(L)	Intestine	internal
(L)	Intoxication	to smear with poison
(L)	Intra	inside
	Intrinsic	special to the thing itself
(L)	Intussusception	within receive
(L)	Invagination	enclose in a sheath
(L)	Involution	to roll up
(G)	Iodine	violet
(G)	Iris	coloured membrane of eye
(G)	Ischaemia	lack of blood supply
(G)	Ischium	bone (part of hip bone)
(G)	Isotonic	equal tension
(G)	Isotope	equal place
(L)	Isthmus	narrow, isthmus of fallopian tube
(L)	Iter	a passage (iter cerebri)
(F)	Jaundice	yellowness
(L)	Jejunum	empty or fasting
(L)	Joint	to join
(L)	Jugular	the throat
	Jugam	yoke
(G)	Karyo	a nut (nucleus)
	Keith	Keith's SA node
	(English anatomist)	
(G)	Keratin	horn-in hairy layer of skin
(G)	Kilo	one thousand

	Klumpke (French neurologist)	Klumpke's paralysis
	Kupffer (Greek anatomist)	Kupffer cell (sinusoids of liver)
	Kymograph	a wave writer
(G)	Kyphosis	hump on back
(L)	Labrum	lip
	Labial	pertaining to lips
(L)	Labour	work
(L)	Lac	milk
(G)	Labyrinth	maze
(L)	Lacrimal	tear
(L)	Lacunae	hollow
(G)	Lambda	inverted Y-shaped suture
(L)	Lamina	a thin plate
(L)	Lancet	a slender spear
	Langerhans (German anatomist)	islet of Langerhans (pancreas)
(L)	Lanugo	first soft hair of beard
(L)	Larva	ghost
(G)	Larynx	upper part of wind pipe
(L)	Latent	to lie hidden
(L)	Laxative	loosening
(Gr)	Lemniscus	bandage
(Gr)	Leprosy	scaly disease
(Gr)	Leptomeninx	tender membrane (pia and arachnoid)
(L)	Lethal	death
(Gr)	Lethargy	forgetful
(Gr)	Leuc	white, leucocyte, leucoplakia, leucorrhoea
(L)	Levator	one who lifts
(L)	Libido	desire, lustre
(G)	Lieberkuhn (German scientist)	crypts of Lieberkuhn (intestine)
	Lienal	spleen
	Ligament	to bind, e.g. deltoid ligament, falciform ligament, etc.
(L)	Limbus	a border
(L)	Limen	edge or threshold - L. insulae
(L)	Linea	a line
(L)	Lingual	the tongue
(S)	Lipoma	fat
(Gr)	Lithos	a stone
(L)	Locus	a place

(G)	Lordosis	increased anterior curvature of lumbar spine
	Louis	Louis's angle of sternum (sternal angle)
	(French physician)	
	Lower	projection in the right atrial wall between the
	(English physician)	two caval openings
(L)	Ludwig	Ludwig's angina
	(German surgeon)	
(L)	Lumbar	loin
	Lumbrical	a worm (a muscle)
(L)	Lumen	light passage
(L)	Lunar	the moon
	Lutein	yellow pigment of corpora lutea
	(German anatomist)	
(L)	Lymph	clear water
(Gr)	Macro	big
	Macroscopic	big to see
(L)	Macula	a small patch (macula lutea, macula densa)
	Magendie	Foramen of Magendie
	(French doctor)	
(G)	Malacia	softness
(F)	Malady	illness
(L)	Malar	cheek bone
	Malaria	bad air
(L)	Malignant	ill-disposed
(L)	Malleus	hammer—ear ossicle
(L)	Malleolus	a little hammer
	Mallory	Mallory's stain
	(Irish anatomist)	
	Malpighi	Malpighian corpuscle, Malpighian layer in
	(Italian anatomist)	skin
	Founder of Histology	
(L)	Mamma	the breast
(L)	Mandible	lower jaw
(Gr)	Mania	madness
(L)	Manubrium	a handle (Manubrium sterni)
(Gr)	Marasmus	waste away
	Marchi	Marchi's staining for nerve fibres
	(Irish anatomist)	
	Marginal	artery border, along large intestine
(L)	Marrow	medulla
	Marshall	Marshall's vein—oblique vein of left atrium
	(English surgeon)	
(Gr)	Masseter	the chewer

(Gr)	Mast	to feed
(Gr)	Mastos	breast
(L)	Mastication	to chew
(L)	Matrix	mould
(L)	Mature	to ripe—maturation
	Maxilla	cheek
	McBurney (American surgeon)	McBurney point for appendicectomy
(L)	Meatus	canal
	Meckel (German anatomist)	Meckel's cave for 5th N. ganglion, Meckel's cartilage
	Meatus	canal
(L)	Median	central
(L)	Mediastinum	middle space
(L)	Medicine	the art of healing
(L)	Medulla	marrow
	Medusa (Greek goddess)	caput medusa
(L)	Mega	big
	Meibom (German anatomist)	meibomian glands
(L)	Meiosis	lessening
	Meissner	Meissner's plexus in submucous coat of GIT
(L)	Melan	black
	Melanin	black pigment
(G)	Meninges	a membrane
	Meningocoele	memb. + hernia
(G)	Meniscus	crescent (med. cat. menisci in knee joint)
(G)	Men (prefix)	month, e.g. menopause, menorrhagia, menstruation, menarche
(Gr)	Merkel	corpuscle sensory nerve ending
(Gr)	Mesencephalon	mid-brain
(Gr)	Mesenchyme	middle infusion or juice
(Gr)	Mesentery	middle intestine
	Mesoderm	middle skin
(G)	Mesonephros	middle kidney
(G)	Mesothelium	middle nipple
(G)	Metacarpus	from wrist
(G)	Metamorphosis	changed form
(G)	Metanephros	after kidney
(G)	Metastasis	removal from one place
(G)	Metencephalon	after brain
(G)	Metopic	frontal, space between eyes—M. suture

(G)	Metre	unit of length
	Meynert	Dorsal teg. decusation
	(Austrian physician)	
(G)	Microbe	small life
(G)	Microcyte	small cell
(G)	Microglia	small glue (cells)
(G)	Micrometer	small measure
(G)	Microscope	small eye-view
(G)	Microtome	small cutting
(G)	Mitochondria	the thread grain
(G)	Mitosis	thread
(L)	Mitral	kind of cap
(G)	Mneomonic	relating to memory
(L)	Molar	milestone—a tooth
(E)	Mole	spot
	Monro	foramen of Monro—interventricular
	(English scientist)	foramen of brain
	Montgomery	Montgomery's tubercles in the nipple
	(Irish obstetrician)	
(L)	Morbid	ill
	Morgagni	appendix of testis
	(Italian anatomist)	
(F)	Morgue	mortuary
	Morison	Morison's pouch (hepatorenal pouch)
	(English surgeon)	
	Moron	dull
(G)	Morphology	shape/discourse
(L)	Morula	mulberry
(L)	Mucus	thin watery fluid, mucosa
	Muller	Muller's muscle in eye (circular), mullerian
	(German anatomist)	duct
(L)	Multiparous	more than once pregnant
(L)	Murmur	a humming sound
(L)	Muscle	a little mouse; myology
(G)	Museum	temple of muses
(L)	Mutation	to change
(L)	Mydriatic	unnatural dilatation of pupil
(G)	Myopia	close to eyes
(G)	Myxoma	mucus + tumor
	Naboth	Nabothian glands
	(German anatomist)	
(L)	Naevus	birth mark
	Nagek	Nagek pelvis (obliquely contracted pelvis)
	(German obstetrician)	

(E)	Nape	ext. depression, knob
	Narcolepsy	numbness
(L)	Nares	nostril, nasal
(G)	Nausea	sickness
(A)	Navel	umbilicus
(L)	Navicular	boat-shaped
(G)	Necrosis	a dead body
(G)	Neo	new
	Neolithic	new stone
	Neoplasm	new form
(G)	Nephr	kidney
	Nephropexy	kidney + fastening
(L)	Nerve	string, N. root
(G)	Neuralgia	pain in nerves
(G)	N. crest	on either side of neural tube
(G)	Neurasthenia	nerve weakness
(G)	Neurilemma	nerve covering
(G)	Neurobiotaxis	nerve + life + arrangement of nerves in living
(L)	Neutrophil	neuter (not fond of any color)
	Nipple	beak
	Nissl	Nissl granules in neurons
	(German neurologist)	
(L)	Nodus	knot
(L)	Nomenclature	a list of names
(G)	Nostalgia	home coming + pain
(G)	Notochord	back + a string
(Ar)	Nucha	spinal cord
(Du)	Nuck	canal of Nuck
(L)	Nucleus	nut
(L)	Nullipara	none + bring forth, not yet pregnant
(L)	Nurse	to nourish
(G)	Nyctalopia	night blindness
(G)	Nystagmus	nodding
(Gr)	Obelian	a pointed pillar portion of sagittal suture between 2 parietal bones
(L)	Obstetrix	midwife
	Obstetrics	Surgery, dealing with pregnancy, labour
	Obturator	a stopper of
	Occiput	back of head
	Occult	hidden
	Oculus	eye
	Oddi	sphincter of Oddi
	(Irish physician)	

(G)	Odontoid	tooth-like
(G)	Oesophagus	gullet
(L)	Oestrus	madness or frenzy
(G)	Olecranon	point of elbow
(L)	Olfaction	to smell
(G)	Oligo	few
(G)	Omohyoid	shoulder + hyoid bone
(G)	Omphalos	omphalocoele (umb.)
(G)	Oopheron	ovary
(L)	Operation	to work
(L)	Operculum	lip
(Gr)	Ophth	eye
(Gr)	Optics	belonging to sight, optic chiasma; optic disc
(L)	Oral	of mouth
(L)	Orbicularis	circular
(G)	Orchitis	testicle inflammations
(L)	Organ	any part of the body with a special function
(Gr)	Osmosis	push
(L)	Ossicle	small bone
(Gr)	Otic	ear, O. ganglion
(L)	Ovary	egg receptacle
(G)	Oxyntic	to make sour
	Pacchioni (Italian anatomist)	arachnoid granulations
(Gr)	Pachymeninx	thick membrane
	Pacini (Italian anatomist)	pacinian corpuscle
(G)	Paediatrics	child + healing
	Paget (English surgeon)	Paget's disease
(G)	Palaco	old
(L)	Pallid	pale
(L)	Pallium	clock or mantle
(L)	Palpate	to touch
(L)	Palpebra	eyelid
	Palsy	paralysis
(L)	Pampiniform	tendril
(G)	Panacea	all healing
(G)	Pan	sweet bread
(G)	Pandemic	all people
(L)	Panniculus	a piece of cloth, a layer of membrane, panniculus carnosus
(L)	Paraffin	little affinity

	Paradidymus	beside + twin-like
(Gr)	Paralysis	weakening
	Parametrium	beside the uterus
	Paraphimosis	constriction of the prepuce behind the glans penis
	Paraplegia	paralysis of lower limbs
	Parenchyma	functional
	Parietal	a wall
	Paronychia	beside nail
	Para	beside
	Passavant (German surgeon)	Passavant's ridge
(L)	Patella	a small dish (sesamoid bone)
(L)	Pecten	a comb
(L)	Pectoral	belonging to breast
(L)	Pedicle	a little foot
	Peduncle	a foot
	Pellagra	skin attack
(L)	Pelvis	a basin
(L)	Penis	tail
(L)	Percussion	beating
(L)	Perforator	to bore through
(G)	Peri	around
(G)	Perilymph	clear watery fluid all around
(G)	Perineum	swim around penis
(G)	Periosteum	around bone
(G)	Periphery	circumference
	Peristalsis	contracting around
	Peritoneum	serous membrane lining abdomen
(G)	Peroneus	anything pointed for piercing
(L)	pes-a foot	hippocampus (foot-like)
(L)	pessary	an oval body (plug)
	Petit (French surgeon)	Petit's triangle
(L)	Petrous	stony, rock, P. temporal bone
	Peyer (Swiss anatomist)	Peyer's patch (ileum)
(G)	Phagocytosis	eat + cell + osis (fullness), i.e., eating cells
(G)	Phalanx	closely knit row
(G)	Pharynx	musculo memb. sac behind the mouth
(L)	Philtrum	a love charm
(Gr)	Phimosis	stopping up (in relation to prepuce of penis)
(Gr)	Phonation	sound or voice

(Gr)	Physiotherapy	nature + treatment
(L)	Pia mater	soft mother
(L)	Pineal	pine cone
(L)	Pinna	ear
(L)	Piriform	pear-shaped
(L)	Pisiform	pea-shaped
(L)	Pituitary	mucus secretion
(L)	Placenta	flat cake
	Planes	flat
	Plantar	sole of foot
(Gr)	Platysma	flat
(Gr)	Pleo	more
(Gr)	Plethora	fullness
(Gr)	Pleura	serous memb. enfolding lung
(L)	Plexus	woven
(L)	Plica	to fold
(L)	Plumbus	lead
(L)	Pneumo	gas
(Gr)	Podagra	foot
(Gr)	Podalic	foot
(L)	Polarity	relating to pole
(Gr)	Polio	grey matter + inflammation
(L)	Pollex	thumb (strong)
(Gr)	Poly	many
(L)	Pons	bridge
(L)	Popliteus	ham
(L)	Porta	gate
(L)	Post	behind
	Poupart	Poupart's ligament (inguinal ligament)
	(French anatomist)	
(L)	Pregnant	with child
(L)	Prepuce	foreskin
(Gr)	Presbyopia	old age hypermetropia
(Gr)	Proposis	elephant's trunk
(L)	Process	advance
(L)	Procidentia	parts that fall out of place
(Gr)	Prodo	anus
(Gr)	Prodromal	in advance
(L)	Progesterone	before to bear
(Gr)	Prognosis	to know beforehand
	Prolapse	falling
	Proliferate	create or reproduce in quick succession
(L)	Promontory	prominence

(L)	Pronator	to bend forward
(Gr)	Pronephros	before kidney
(Gr)	Prophylaxis	to keep guard (the prevention of a disease)
(L)	Proprioceptive	one's own, to take
(Gr)	Prosencephalon	forward + brain
(Gr)	Prostate	before + stand
(Gr)	Prosthetic	in addtion
(Gr)	Protamine	first + amine
(Gr)	Protein	comprised of amino acid
(Gr)	Protocol	first glue
(Gr)	Protopathic	first + suffering
(L)	Pruritis	itching
(Gr)	Psoas	loin
	Psyche	breath
(Gr)	Pterion	wing
(Gr)	Pterygoid	wing-like
(Gr)	Ptoma	a corpse
(Gr)	Ptosis	falling
(Gr)	Ptyalin	saliva
(L)	Pubis	puberty
(L)	Pud	to be ashamed (pudendal)
(L)	Puerperal	after delivery
(E)	Puke	to vomit
(L)	Pul (prefix)	lung
(L)	Puke	beating
(L)	Pulvinar	cushion, pillow
(L)	Punctum	point
(L)	Putamen	cutting
(Gr)	Pyelo	basin
(Gr)	Pylorus	gatekeeper
(Gr)	Pyramid	swelling
(Gr)	Pyrexia	fever
(L)	Quadri	four
	Quadratus	square
	Quadriceps/quadri	geminus four heads/two twins
(G)	Quartz	rock crystal
(L)	Rabies	rage/madness
(L)	Racemose	cluster of grapes (glands)
(Gr)	Rachitis	spine
(L)	Radical	roots
(L)	Radium	radioactive element
(L)	Radius	small bone of forearm
(L)	Ramus	branch

	Ranvier (French histologist)	node of Ranvier
(Gr)	Raphe	suture
(L)	Rash	eruption of skin
	Rathke (German anatomist)	Rathke's pouch
(L)	Receptor	to receive
(L)	Rectum	upright (misnomer)
(L)	Recurrent	running back
(L)	Refraction	broken (bend)
	Reid (Scottish anatomist)	R. base (from lower margin of orbit through centre of ext. aud. meatus)
	Reil (Greek physiologist)	island of Reil-Insula
	Reissner (Greek anatomist)	R. fibres running through the length of brainstem and spinal cord
	Remarc (German neurologist)	R. fibre/non-medullated nerve fibre
(L)	Resection	cut off
(L)	Resin	to flow
(L)	Restiform body	rope-shape (inferior cerebellar peduncle)
(L)	Rete	a net, R. mirabile – a wonderful network, R. testis – tubular network
(L)	Reticulum	a little net
(L)	Retinaculum	to hold back
(L)	Retort	twisted back
(L)	Retro (prefix)	behind, retroverted, retroflexed uterus, retroph. space
	Retzius (Swedish scientist)	space of Retzius
(Gr)	Rheumatism	a liability
(Gr)	Rhinencephalon	nose + brain
(Gr)	Rhinoplasty	nose moulding
(Gr)	Rhomboid	rhombus-like
(Gr)	Rhonchus	snoring
(L)	Rigor	rigidity
(L)	Rima	slit, rima glottidis
(L)	Risus	to laugh, risus sardonicus
	Robertson (Scottish ophthalmologist)	Argyll Robertson pupil (pupil sign)
	Robin (German histologist)	perivas/space in brain

	Rolando (Italian anatomist)	fissure of Rolando
	Rosenmuller (German anatomist)	fossa of Rosenmuller (Lat. pharyngeal recess)
(L)	Rostrum	beak of a bird
(L)	Rebella	red
	Ruffini (Italian anatomist)	nerve endings of skin
(L)	Rugat	wrinkled
(L)	Saccharin	sugar
(L)	Sacrum	holy
(L)	Sagittal	arrow
(Gr)	Salpina	trumpet
	Santorini (Italian anatomist)	Santorini's cartilage, Santorini's duct accessory duct of pancreas
(Gr)	Saphenous	clear, easily seen. S. vein
(Gr)	Sarco	flesh, sarcolemma
(L)	Sartorius	tailor
(L)	Scala	stairway (scala tympani, scala vestibuli)
(Gr)	Scalenus	irregular
(L)	Scalpel	knife
(Gr)	Scaphoid	boat-shaped
(L)	Scapula	shoulder blades
	Scarpa Italian anatomist)	Scarpa's fascia, (deeper membranous layer of sup. fascia) Scarpa's ganglia 8th N. ganglia
(Gr)	Schizophrenia	split mind
	Schlemm (German anatomist)	Schlemm's canal at corneo-scleral junction
	Schwann (German anatomist)	cell of Schwann
(L)	Sciatica	pain in loins
(L)	Scirrhus	hard
(Gr)	Sclera	hard
(Gr)	Scoliosis	curvature (lateral)
(L)	Scrotum	skin or hide
(L)	Sebum	grease
(L)	Segmentation	to cut
(L)	Sella turcica	Turkish saddle
(L)	Semen	that which is sown
(L)	Semi	half
(L)	Septum	a dividing wall
(L)	Serratus	like saw
(Gr)	Sesamoid	seed-like (patella)

	Sharpey (English anatomist)	Sharpey's fibres in compact bone
	Sibson	S. fascia
(Gr)	Sigmoid	sigma-like
	Sims position	lithotomy position
(L)	Sinus	anything hollowed out
(Gr)	Skeleton	dried up
(L)	Soleus	sole
(Gr)	Soma	body
(L)	Soporific	deep sleep
(L)	Spatula	flat wooden instrument
(Gr)	Sperm	seed
	Sphenoid	butterfly shaped
(Gr)	Sphincter	bind/tight
(L)	Spine	thorn
(Gr)	Splanchnic	relating to bowels
(Gr)	Splenius	bandage
(Gr)	Spondylitis	vertebra inflammation
(Gr)	Spondylolisthesis	vet + sliding
(L)	Squama	scale of fish
(L)	Stapes	stirrup (ear ossicle)
(Gr)	Stasis	standing
(Gr)	Stenosis	narrowing
	Stensen (Danish anatomist)	Stensen's duct, parotid gland duct
(Gr)	Stethoscope	instrument of listening the ausculatory sounds
(L)	Stimulus	to prick
(Gr)	Stoma	mouth
(Gr)	Stomach	mouth bed
(Gr)	Strabismus	squinting
(L)	Stratum	covering
(L)	Stria	furrow
(L)	Stricture	contraction
(L)	Strider	harsh
(Gr)	Stroma	bed
(Gr)	Styloid	pointed
(L)	Sub	under
(L)	Subclavian	under clavicle
(L)	Substantia	essence
(L)	Sudor	sweat
(L)	Sulcus	furrow
(L)	Super	over, above
(L)	Supination	bent backwards

(L)	Sural	calf of leg
(Gr)	Surgeon	hand + work (operator)
(L)	Sustentaculum	support (sustentacular tali)
(L)	Stitch	sewing together
	Sylvius (German anatomist)	Sylvius' fissure, Lat. fissure of the brain
(Gr)	Symbiosis	living with
(Gr)	Symphysis	natural union
(Gr)	Syndrome	running together
(G)	Synovia	along with + egg
(L)	Syringe	like a pipe (tube)
(Gr)	Syringomyelia	pipe + marrow
(Gr)	Systole	contraction
(L)	Tabes	wasting away
(Gr)	Taenia	rope-like structure, T. thalami, T. coli, hookworms
(L)	Talipes	weak on feet
(L)	Talus	ankle bone
(L)	Tapetum	carpet
(Gr)	Tarsus	Crate – bones of post. part of foot
(L)	Tectum	to cover
(Gr)	Telangiectesis	end vessel dilatation
(L)	Tellurium	earth
(L)	Temple (temporal)	temple region
(L)	Tendon	to stretch out
	Tenon (German surgeon)	T. capsule (back of eyeball)
(L)	Tensor	stretch out
(I.)	Tentorium	tent
(L)	Teres	round
(L)	Testicle	testis (singular)
(Gr)	Tetanus	stretch, tetany
(Gr)	Thalamus	inner chamber
(Gr)	Thallium	young
	Thebesius (German physician)	Thebesian valve, valve of coronary sinus
(Gr)	Thenar	the part of the hand with which one strikes
(Gr)	Theory	speculation
(Gr)	Therapy	care
(Gr)	Thrombus	rump
(L)	Thymus	leaf used for worship
(Gr)	Thyroid	shield (oblong)
(L)	Tibia	shin bone (flute)

Gr)	Tissue	woven
(Gr)	Tone	which can be stretched
(A)	Tooth	an organ of mastication
(Gr)	Topography	a place + description
(L)	Torticollis	twisted
(L)	Torus	bulging place
(Gr)	Tourniquet	instrument for turning
(Gr)	Toxin	poison
(L)	Trabeculae	a little beam
(Gr)	Trachea	wind pipe
(L)	Tract	pathway
(Gr)	Tragus	ear
(L)	Transfusion	pouring out
	Trapezium	table
(Gr)	Trauma	wound
	Treitz (Austrian physician)	lig of Treitz at duo-jej.flexure
(Gr)	Trema	hole
(L)	Tremor	shaking
	Trendelenburg (German surgeon)	Trendelenburg's position, Trendelenburg's sign and Trendelenburg's test
	Trephine	a saw for cutting out circular piece of bone esp. skull
	Treves (English surgeon)	bloodless fold of Treves
(L)	Triceps	having three heads
(Gr)	Trichiasis	hair (trichionis)
(Gr)	Tricuspid	three cusps
(L)	Trigeminal	three + twin-like (3 divisions)
(Gr)	Trigone	triangle
(L)	Triquetral	having 3 corners
(Gr)	Trocar	3 quarters
(Gr)	Trochanter	bony process
(L)	Trochlea	pulley
(Gr)	Trophic	nourishment (trophoblast)
(Gr)	Tropism	burning
(L)	Tube	a trumpet
(L)	Tumour	swelling
(L)	Turbinate	spinning top
(L)	Tympanum	kettle drum
	Typhoid	fever typhus like
	Tyson (English anatomist)	Tyson's glands, seb. glands on inner side of prepuce

(L)	Ulcer	sore
(L)	Ulna	elbow
(L)	Umbilicus	naval
	Umbo	tymp. membrane
(L)	Unciform	hook-shaped
(L)	Undulant	fever, wave
(Gr)	Urachus	urinary canal of foetus
(Gr)	Uranium	heaven
(Gr)	Ureter	urinary duct
(Gr)	Urethra	to make water
(Gr)	Urobilin	urine + bile
(L)	Urticaria	to burn
(L)	Uterus	womb
	Utricle	a little uterus
(L)	Uvea	grape
(L)	uvula	a little grape
(L)	Vaccine	lymph from cow-pox vesicle
(L)	Vagina	sheath
(L)	Vagus	vagabond (wanderer)
(L)	Valency	capacity
	Valentine (German physician)	discovered nucleolus and sex cords of ovary
	Valentine (German anatomist)	V. bodies in N. tissue
(L)	Valgus	bow-legged
	Valsalva (Italian anatomist)	Valsalva sinuses aortic sinuses
(L)	Valve	leaf of folding door
(L)	Varix (varicose)	dilated veins
	Varolius (Italian anatomist)	pons varolii
(L)	Varus	grown inwards, knock knee – genu varus
(L)	Vas	vessel
(L)	Vastus	large
	Vater (German anatomist)	ampulla of Vater
(L)	Vector	one that bears
(L)	Velum	curtain
(L)	Venereal	belonging to Venus (goddess of love)
(L)	Venter	belly, ventricle
(L)	Vermis	worm
(L)	Vertebra	turning place or joint
(L)	Vertigo	to turn around

	Vesalius (Belgian anatomist)	Father of Anatomy
(L)	Vesica	bladder
(L)	Vestibule	enclosed space
(L)	Vestigeal	remnant of something formerly present
(L)	Veterinary	cattle doctor
	Vidius (Italian physician)	vidian nerve, nerve of pterygoid canal
(L)	Villus	tuft of hair
	Virchow (German pathologist)	V. robin space
(L)	Virus	poison
(L)	Viscus/viscera	vital organ/plural
(L)	Vision	act of seeing
(L)	Vital	to life
(L)	Vitamin	life + amine
(L)	Vitelline	yolk of egg
(L)	Vocal cords	uttering of voice
(L)	Volar	palm of hand
	Volkmann (German physician)	V. canal
(L)	Voluntary	willing
(L)	Volvulus	to roll
(L)	Vomer	thin plate of bone between nostrils
(L)	Vulva	to roll, to turn around
	Waldeyer (German anatomist)	W. ring at oropharyngeal isthmus
	Waller (English physician)	Wallerian nerve degeneration
	Westphal (German neurologist)	W. nucleus (part of oculomotor complex)
	Wharton (English anatomist)	W. duct (Submand. duct), Wharton's jelly
	Whisky	water of life
	Whitlow	painful swelling in finger
(E)	Whooping cough	to call/shout
	Widal (French physician)	W. reaction
	Willis (English Anatomist)	circle of Willis
	Winslow (Danish anatomist)	foramen of Winslow
	Wirsung	pancreatic duct

	(German anatomist)	
	Wistar	pyramids (in kidneys)
	(American anatomist)	
	Wolff	Wolfian or mesonephric
	(German anatomist)	
	Wright	W. stain
	(American anatomist)	
(Gr)	Xanthine	yellow
	Xeroderma	dry or parched
(Gr)	Xiphoid	sword-like
	Xylol	wood + oil
	Yellow fever	an infectious viral fever
	Young	Young's rule
	(English physician)	
	Zenker	Zenker's solution
	(German histologist)	
	Zinn	annulus of Zinn (origin of rectus)
	(German anatomist)	
(L)	Zona	zone
(Gr)	Zoology	animal + treatise
	Zuckerkandl	Zuckerkandl's gyrus, subcallosal gyrus
	(Austrian anatomist)	
	Zygoma	like a yoke
	Zymogen	ferment producer, Z. granules in serous acini

References and Suggestions for Additional Reading

CHAPTER 1

Field, E.J. and Harrison, R.J. (1957). *Anatomical Terms, their Origin and Derivation,* 2nd edn. Heffer, Cambridge.

Major, R.H. (1954). *A History of Medicine,* 2 volumes. Thomas, Springfield.

Singer, C., (1957). *A Short History of Anatomy from the Greeks to Harvey.* Dover, New York.

Singh, S. (1972). Grave-robbers all. *Science Reporter,* 9: 492–493.

Singh, S. (1972). The Illustrious Hunters and the Anatomy Museums. *Indian Med. Gaz.,*12: 62–66.

Singh, S. (1973). Cadaveric supply for anatomical dissections, a historical review. *Indian J. History Med.* 18: 35–39.

Singh, S. (1974). Susruta, pioneer in human dissections. *Souvenir, Anat. Soc. India,* 31–32.

CHAPTER 2

Athawale, M.C. (1963). Estimation of height from lengths of forearm bones: A study of one hundred Maharashtrian male adults of ages between twenty-five and thirty years. *Am. J. Phys. Anthropol.,* 21: 105 11 2.

Bajaj, I.D., Bhardwaj, O.P. and Bhardwaj, S. (1967). Appearance and fusion of important ossification centres: A study of Delhi population. *Indian J. Med. Res.,* 55: 1064–1067.

Berry, A.C. (1975). Factors affecting the incidence of non-metrical skeletal variants. *J. Anat.,* 120: 519–535.

Brahma, K.C. and Mitra, N.L. (1973). Ossification of carpal bones: A radiological study in the tribals of Chotanagpur. *J. Anat. Soc. India,* 22: 21–28.

Charnalia, V.M. (1961). Anthropological study of the foot and its relationship to stature in different castes and tribes of Pondicherry State. *J. Anat. Soc. India,* 10: 26–30.

Chhatrapati, D.N. and Misra, B.D. (1967). Position of the nutrient foramen on the shafts of human long bones. *J. Anat. Soc. India, 16: 1–10*

Das Gupta, S.M., Prasad, V. and Singh, S. (1974). A roentgenologic study of epiphysial union around elbow, wrist and knee joints and the pelvis in boys and girls of Uttar Pradesh. *J. Indian Med. Assoc.,* 62: 10–12.

Garg, K., Bahl, I., Mathur, R. and Verma, R.K. (1985). Bilateral asymmetry in surface area of carpal bones in children. *J. Anat. Soc. Ind.* 34: 167–172.

Garg, K., Kulshrestha, V., Bahl, I., Mathur, R, Mitta, S.K. and Verma, R. (1988). Asymmetry in surface area of capitate and hamate bones in normal and malnourished children. *J. Anat. Soc. Ind.* 37: 73–74.

Gupta, A., Garg, K., Mathur, R. and Mittal, S.K. (1988). Asymmetry in surface area of bony epiphysis of knee in normal and malnourished children. *Ind. Paed.* No. 10: 999–1000.

Halim, A. and Siddiqui M.S. (1976). Sexing of atlas. *Indian J. Phys. Anthropol. Hum. Genet.,* 2: 129–135.

Hasan, M. and Narayan, D. (1963). The ossification centres of carpal bones: A radiological study of the times of appearance in U.P. Indian subjects. *Indian J. Med. Res.,* 51: 917–920.

Hasan, M. and Narayan, D. (1964). Radiological study of the postnatal ossification of the upper end of humerus in U.P. Indians. *J. Anat. Soc. India,* 13: 70–75.

Jeyasingh, P., Saxena, S.K., Arora, A.K., Pandey, D.N. and Gupta, C.D. (1980). A study of correlations between some neonatal and placental parameters. *J. Anat. Soc. India,* 29: 14–18.

Jit, I. (1957). Observations on prenatal ossification with special reference to the bones of hand and foot. *J. Anat. Soc. India,* 6: 12–23.

Jit, I. (1972). Times of ossification in India (editorial). *Bull. PGI (Chandigarh),* 6: 100–103.

Jit, I. (1979). The house of skeletons case. *J. Anat. Soc. India,* 28: 106–116.

Jit, I., Jhingan, V. and Kulkarni, M. (1980). Sexing of human sternum. *Am. J. Phys. Anthropol.,* 53: 217–224.

Jit, I. and Gandhi, O.P. (1966). The value of preauricular sulcus in sexing bony pelvis. *J. Anat. Soc. India,* 15: 104–107.

Jit, I. and Kulkarni, M. (1976). Times of appearance and fusion of epiphysis at the medial end of the clavicle. *Indian J. Med. Res.,* 64: 773–782.

Jit, I. and Singh, S. (1956). Estimation of the stature from the clavicle. *Indian J. Med. Res.,* 44: 133–135.

Jit, I. and Singh, S. (1966). Sexing of the adult clavicle. *Indian J. Med. Res.,* 54: 551–571.

Jit, I. and Singh, B. (1971). A radiological study of the time of fusion of certain epiphyses in Punjabees. *J. Anat. Soc. India,* 20: 1–27.

Jit, I., Verma, U. and Gandhi, O.P. (1968). Ossification of bones of the hand and foot in newborn children. *J. Anat. Soc. India,* 17: 8–13.

Kate, B.R. (1964). A study of the regional variation of the Indian femur, the diameter of the head, its medicolegal and surgical application. *J. Anat. Soc. India,* 13: 80–84.

Kate, B.R. (1967). The angle of the femoral neck in Indians. *East. Anthropologist,* 20: 54–60.

Kate, B.R. (1971). Nutrient foramina in human long bones. *J. Anat. Soc. India,* 20: 139–144.

Kate, B.R and Majumdar, R.D. (1976). Stature estimation from femur and humerus by regression and autometry. *Acta Anat.,* 94: 311–320.

Kolte, P.M. and Bansal, P.C. (1974). Determination of regression formulae for reconstruction of stature from the long bones of upper limb in Maharashtrians of Marathwada region. *J. Anat. Soc. India,* 23: 6–11.

Krogman, W.M. (1962). *The Human Skeleton in Forensic Medicine.* Thomas, Springfield, Ill.

Longia, G.S., Ajmani, M.L., Saxena, S.K. and Thomas, R.J. (1980). Study of diaphysial nutrient foramina in the human long bones. *Acta Anat.,* 107: 399–406.

Maniar, B.M., Seervai, M.H. and Kapur, P.L. (1974). A study of ossification centres in the hand and wrist of Indian children. *Indian Pediatr.,* II: 203–211.

Modi, N.J. (1977). *Modi's Textbook of Medical Jurisprudence and Toxicology,* 20th edn, pp. 27–38 and 80–88, Tripathi, Bombay.

Mysorekar, V.R. (1967). Diaphysia nutrient foramina in human long bones. *J. Anat.,* 101: 813–822.

Mysorekar, V.R. and Nandedkar, A.N. (1979). Diaphysial nutrient foramina in human phalanges. *J. Anat.,* 128: 315–322.

Mysorekar, V.R., Verma, P.K., Nandedkar, A.N. and Sarma, T.C.S.R. (1980). Estimation of stature from parts of bones, lower end of femur and upper end of radius. *Medicine Science and Law (Lond.),* 20: 283–286.

Mysorekar, V.R., Nandedkar, A.N. and Sarma, T.C.S.R. (in press). Estimation of stature from parts of humerus and radius. *Medicine. Science and Law (Lond.).*

Narayan, D. and Bajaj, J.D. (1957). Ages of epiphysial union in long bones of inferior extremity in U.P. subjects. *Indian J. Med. Res.,* 45: 645–649.

Patake, S.M. and Mysorekar, V.R. (1977). Diaphysial nutrient foramina in human metacarpals and metatarsals. *J. Anat.,* 124: 299–304.

Pillai, M.J.S. (1936). The study of epiphysial union for determining the age of South Indians. *Indian J. Med. Res.,* 23; 1015–1017.

Prakash, S., Chopra, S.R.K. and Jit, I. (1979). Ossification of the human patella. *J. Anat. Soc. India,* 28: 78–83.

Qamra, SR, Jit, I. and Deodhar, S.D. (1980). A mode for reconstructing height from foot measurements in an adult population of north-west India. *Indian J. Med. Res.,* 71; 77–83.

Raju, P.B. and Singh, S. (1978). Sexual dimorphism in scapula. *J. Indian Acad. Forens. Sci.,* 17: 23–34.

Raju, B.P. and Singh, S. (1979). Sexual dimorphism in hip bone. *Indian J. Med. Res.,* 69; 849–855.

Raju, P.B., Singh, S. and Padmanabhan, R. (1981). Sex determination and sacrum. *J. Anat. Soc. India,* 30: 13–15.

Saxena, S.K., Jeyasingh, P., Gupta. A.K. and Gupta, C.D. (1981). Estimation of stature from measurement of head length. *J. Anat. Soc. India,* 30: 78–79.

Saxena, S.K., Maewal, S., Pandey, D.N. and Gupta, C.D. (1981). A study of correlationships between CR length and neonatal and placental parameters. *J. Anat. Soc. India,* 30: 67–69.

Siddiqui, M.A.H. and Shah, M.A. (1944). Estimation of stature from long bones of Punjabees. *Indian J. Med. Res.,* 32: 105–108.

Singh, B. and Sohal, H.S. (1952). Estimation of stature from the length of clavicle in Punjabees, a preliminary report. *Indian J. Med. Res.,* 40: 67–71.

Singh, G., Singh, S. (1976). Identification of sex from the fibula. *J. Indian Acad. Forens. Sci.,* 15: 29–34.

Singh G., Singh, S.P. and Singh, S. (1974). Identification of sex from the radius. *J. Indian Acad. Forens. Sci.,* 13: 10–16.

Singh, G., Singh, S. and Singh, S.P. (1975). Identification of sex from tibia. *J. Anat. Soc. India,* 24: 20–24.

Singh, I. (1978). The architecture of cancellous bone. *J. Anat.,* 127: 305–310.

Singh, S. and Gangrade, K.C. (1968). The sexing of adult clavicles. Demarking points for Varanasi zone. *J. Anat. Soc. India,* 17: 89–100.

Singh S. and Potturi, B.R. (1978). Greater sciatic notch in sex determination. *J. Anat.,* 127: 619–624.

Singh, S. and Raju, P.B. (1977). Identification of sex from the hip bone, demarking points. *J. Anat. Soc. India,* 26: 111–117.

Singh, S. and Singh, S.P. (1972). Identification of sex from the humerus. *Indian J. Med. Res.,* 60: 1061–1066.

Singh, S. and Singh, S.P. (1974). Weight of the femur, a useful measurement for identification of sex. *Acta Anat.,* 87: 141–145.

Singh, S. and Singh, S.P. (1975). Identification of sex from tarsal bones. *Acta Anat.,* 93: 568–573.

Singh S., Singh, G. and Singh, S.P. (1974). Identification of sex from the ulna. *Indian J. Med. Res.,* 62: 731–735.

Singh S.P. and Singh, S. (1972 a). The sexing of adult femora, demarking points for Varanasi zone. *J. Indian Acad. Forens. Sci.,* 11: 1–6.

Singh S.P.. and Singh, S. (1972 b). Identification of sex from the head of a femur, the demarking points of Varanasi zone. *Indian Med. Gaz.,* 12: 45–49.

Srivastava, K.K., Pai, R.A., Kolbhandari, M.P. and Kant, K. (1971). Cleidocranial dysostosis: A clinical and cytological study. *Clin. Genet.,* 2: 104–110.

Tandon, B.K. (1964). A study of the vascular foramina at the two ends of ulna. *J. Anat. Soc. India,* 13: 24–27.

Ujwal, Z.S. (1962). Nutrient canal of long bones. *Univ. Rajasthan Studies,* 6: 39–43.

Vare, A.M. and Bansal, P.C. 1977). Estimation of crown–rump length from diaphysial lengths of foetal long bones. *J. Anat. Soc. India,* 26: 91–93.

CHAPTER 3

Barnett, C.H., Davies, D.V. and MacConail, M.A. (1961). *Synovial Joints: Their Structure and Mechanics.* Longmans, London.

Freeman, M.A.R. (1973). *Adult Articular Cartilag.* Pitman Medical, London.

Gardner, E.D. (1948). The innervation of the knee joint. *Anat. Rec.,* 101: 109–131; The innervation of the shoulder joint. *Anat. Rec.,* 102: 1–18, 1948.

Hilton, J. (1891). *Rest and Pain,* Ed. by W.H.A. Jacobson, reprinted from the last London edition, P.W. Garfield, Cincinnati.

Kapandji, I.A. (1970). *The Physiology of the Joints.* Livingstone, London.

Kellgren, J.H. and Sarnual, E.P. (1950). Sensitivity and innervation of the articular capsule. *J. Bone Jt. Surg.,* 32b: 84–92.

MacConail, M.A. (1932). The function of intra-articular fibrocartilages, with special reference to the knee and inferior radio-ulnar joints. *J. Anat.,* 66: 210–227.

MacConail, M.A. and Basmajian, J.V. (1977). *Muscles and Movements.* Krieger Publishing Company, New York.

Steindler, A. (1955). *Kinesiology of the Human Body.* Thomas, Springfield, Ill.

CHAPTER 4

Basmajian, J.V. (1967). *Muscles Alive,* 2nd edn. Williams and Wilkins, Baltimore.

Burke, R.E., Levine, D. and Tsiaris, P. (1973). Physiological types and histochemical profiles in motor units of the cat gastrocnemius. *J. Physiol., Lond.,* 234: 723–748.

Dubowitz, V. (1969). Histochemical aspects of muscle disease. In: *Disorders of voluntary Muscle* (Walton, J.N. ed.), Churchill, London.

Gauthier, G.F. and Schaeffer, S.F. (1974). Ultrastructural and cytochemical manifestations of protein synthesis in the peripheral sarcoplasm of denervated and newborn skeletal muscle fibres. *J. Cell Sci.,* 143: 113–137.

Jaya, Y. (1957). A brief exposition of AVA, histologically and radiologically. *Proc. Acad. Med. Sc., Hyderabad,* 1: 15–21.

Jaya, Y. (1962). Quantitative anatomy of the capillaries in the rat muscles. *J. Anat. Soc. India,* 11: 32–34.

Kate, B.R. (1971). The cartilage modification of the periosteum. *J. Anat. Soc. India,* 20: 28–32.

MacConail, M.A. and Basmajian, J.V. (1977). *Muscles and Movements.* Krieger Publishing Company, New York.

Sadasivan, G. and Hanmant Rao, G. (1964). Arteriovenous anastomosis in skeletal muscle. *J. Anat. Soc. India,* 13: 90–95.

CHAPTER 5

Bennett, H.S., Luft, J.S. and Hampton, J.C. (1957). Morphological classification of vertebrate blood capillaries. *Am. J. Physiol.,* 196: 381–390.

Clark, E.R. (1938). Arteriovenous anastomosis. *Physiol. Rev.,* 18: 229–247.

Grant, R.T. and Payling Wright, H. (1970). Anatomical basis for non-nutritive circulation is skeletal muscle exemplified by blood vessels of rat biceps femoris tendon. *J. Anat.,* 106: 125–134.

Rhodin, J.A.G. (1962). The diaphragm of capillary endothelial fenestrations. *J. Ullrastruct. Res.,* 6: 171–185.

Rhodin, J.A.G. (1967). Ultrastructure of mammalian arterioles and precapillary sphincters. *J. Ultrastruct. Res.,* 18: 181–223.

Rhodin, J.A.G. (1968). Ultrastructure of mammalian venous capillaries, venules and small collecting veins. *J. Ultrastruct. Res.,* 25: 452–500.

Simionescu, N., Simionescu, M. and Palade, G.E. (1975). Permeability of muscle capillaries to small hemepeptides. Evidence for the existence of patent transendothelial channels. *J. Cell Biol.,* 64: 586–607.

Zweifach, B.W. (1959). The microcirculation of the blood. *Scient. Am.,* 200; 54–60.

CHAPTER 6

Allen, L. (1967) Lymphatics and lymphoid tissue. *A. Rev. Physiol.*, 29: 197–12.4.

Boggon, R.P. and Palfrey, A.J. (1973). The microscopic anatomy of human lymphatic trunks. *J. Anat.*, 114: 389–405.

Jamieson, J.K. and Dobson, J .F. (1910). On the injection of lymphatics by Prussian blue. *J. Anat.*, 45: 7–10; *Lancet,* 1: 1061–1066, 1907; *Proc. R. Soc. Med.*, 2: 149–174, 1908; *Lancet,* 1: 493–495, 1910; *Br. J. Surg.*, 8: 80–87, 1920.

Kinmonth, J.B. (1964). Some general aspects of the investigation and surgery of the lymphatic system. *J. Cardiovasc. Surg.*, 5: 680–682.

Nopajaroonskri, C., Luk, S.C. and Simon, G.T. (1971). Ultrastructure of the normal lymph node. *Am. J. Path.*, 65.: 1–24.

Roitt, I.M. (1977). *Essential Immunology,* 3rd edn. Blackwell, Oxford.

Shridhar (1964). Roentgenographic visualization of human lymphatics, *J. Anat. Soc. India,* 13: 15–17.

Steinman, R.M., Lustig, D.S. and Cohn, Z.A. (1974). Identification of a novel cell type in peripheral lymphoid organs of mice. II. Functional properties in vitro. *J. Exp. Med.*, 139: 380–397.

William, P.L. and Warwick, R. (1980). *Gray's Anatomy,* 36th edn. Churchill Livingstone, London.

CHAPTER 7

Glees, P. and Hasan, M. (1976). *Lipofuscin in Neuronal Aging and Diseases.* Georg Thieme Verlag, Stuttgart.

Glees, P., Hasan, M. and Tischner, K. (1966). Trans-synaptic atrophy in the lateral geniculate body of the monkeys. *J. Physiol. (Lond.)* 188: 17–19.

Grey, E.G. Morphology of synapses. *J. Anat.*, 93: 420–423, 1959; *J. Anat.*, 95: 345–356, 1961; *Prog. Brain Res.*; 31: 141–155, 1969; In: *Essays on the Nervous System* (Bellairs, R. and Gray, E.G., Eds). Clarendon Press, Oxford, 1974.

Gregson, N.A. (1975). The chemistry of myelin. In: *The Peripheral Nerve* (London, D.N., Ed.). Chapman & Hall, London.

Hasan, M., Glees, P. and Tischner, K. (1967). Electron microscopic observations on myelin degeneration in the lateral geniculate body of blinded monkeys. *J. Anat. Soc. India,* 16: 1–11.

Hasan, M. and Glees, P. (1972). Oligodendrocytes in the normal and chronically de-afferented lateral geniculate body of the monkeys. Z. *Zellforsch.*, 135: 115–127.

Hasan, M. and Glees, P. (1972). Electron microscopic appearance of neuronal lipofuscin using different preparative techniques freeze-etching. *Exp. Geront.,* 7: 345–351.

Hasan, M. and Glees, P. (1972). Genesis and possible dissolution of neuronal lipofuscin. *Gerontologia,* 18: 217–236.

Hasan, M. and Glees, P. (1974). Electron microscopic study of the changes in fibrous astrocytes of the lateral geniculate body of blinded monkeys. *J. Anat. Soc. India,* 23: 1–4.

Hasan, M., Shipstone, A.C. and Bajpai, V.K. (1978). Scanning electron microscopy of ventricular ependyma. *Bull. Electron Microscopic Soc. India,* 2: 1–2.

Jacobs, S. and Jacob, M. (1971). Intersegmental anastomoses between adjacent dorsal roots of spinal cord in the human. *Neurol. India,* 19: 51–54.

Jacob, M. and Weddell, G. (1975). Neural intersegmental connections in the spinal roots and ganglion region of the rat. *J. Comp. Neurol.,* 161: 115–123.

Linge, E.A. et al (1973). Identification of glial cells in the brain of young rats. *J. Comp. Neurol.,* 146: 43–72.

Palay, S.L. and Chan Palay, V. (1977). General morphology of neurons and neuroglia. In: *Handbook of Physiology* (Kandel, E.R., Ed.), Vol. 1, Part 2. Physiological Society, Bethesda.

Shepherd, G.M. (1974). *The Synaptic Organization of the Brain.* Oxford University Press, New York.

Singh, I. (1982). *A Textbook of Human Neuroanatomy.* Vikas, New Delhi.

Varon, S. and Bunge, R.P. (1978). Trophic mechanisms in the peripheral nervous system. *Ann. Rev. Neurosci.,* 1: 327–361.

Williams, P.L. and Hall, S.M. (1971). Prolonged in vivo observations of normal peripheral nerve fibres and their acute reactions to crush and local trauma. *J. Anat.,* 108: 397–408.

CHAPTER 8

Cummins, H. and Midlo, C. (1961). *Finger Prints, Palms and Soles: An Introduction to Dermatoglyphics.* Dover, New York.

Montagna, W. and Lobitz, W.C. (1964). *The Epidermis.* Academic Press, New York.

Montagna, W. and Parakkal, P.F. (1974). *The Structure and Function of Skin,* 3rd edn. Academic Press, New York.

Sinclair, D. (1967). *Cutaneous Sensation.* Oxford University Press, London.

Zelickson, A.S. (1967). *Ultrastructure of Normal and Abnormal Skin.* Kimpton, London.

Zelickson, A.S. (1971). Ultrastructure of the human epidemis. In: *Modern Trends in Dermatology* (Borrie, P., Ed.), Volume 4, Butterworth, London.

CHAPTER 9

Garg, K., Bahl, I. and Kaul M. (1991). *A Textbook of Histology.* CBS Publishers & Distributors, New Delhi.

Mitra, N.L. (1979). *A Short Textbook of Histology.* Scientific Book Agency, Calcutta.

Ramachandran, G.N. (1967). *Treatise on Collagen.* Academic Press, New York.

Serafini-Fracassini, A. and Smith, J.W. (1974). *The Structure and Biochemistry of Cartilage.* Churchill-Livingstone, Edinburgh, London.

Wagner, B.M. and Smith, D.E. (1967). *The Connective Tissue,* Williams & Wilkins, Baltimore.

CHAPTER 10

Griffiths, H.J. and Sarno, R.C. (1979). *Contemporary Radiography. An Introduction to Imaging.* Saunders, Philadelphia.

Halim, A. (1993). *Surface and Radiological Anatomy,* 2nd edn. CBS, New Delhi.

Index